MIND BOGGLING PUZZLES

THE BEANO books
geddes & grosset

What a mix-up! How many comic characters can you see in this jumbled-up picture?
ANSWER
Eleven.

Everyone knows Gnasher is an Abyssinian Wire Haired Tripe Hound, but can you rearrange these letters to unscramble some other dogs' names.

1. O DO HOLD BUN

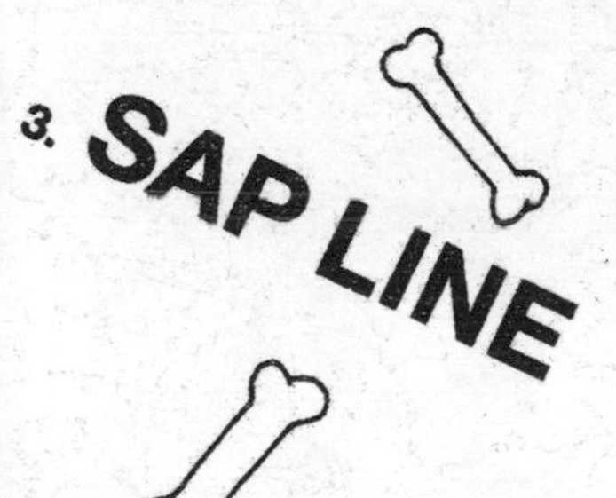

3. SAP LINE

2. A DEAR LIE

4. ERR RITE

5. ICE LOL

6. LOOPED

ANSWER

BLOODHOUND, AIREDALE, SPANIEL, TERRIER, COLLIE, POODLE.

You always get twice the fun with Cuddles and Dimples, but can you spot 6 differences between these two pictures?

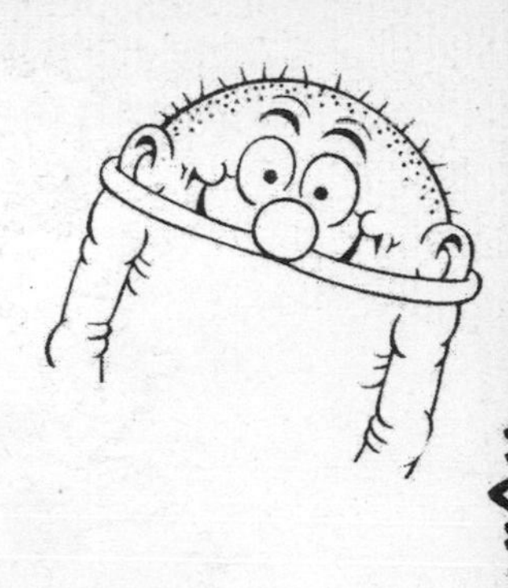

One quarter of the letters in . . . (DREW)
. . . and a half of those in . . . (BILL)
. . . and two fifths of . . . (FREDA)
. . . and one third of . . . (INGRID)
. . . spell one of our names.
Which is it?

ANSWER
Wilfrid.

Unscramble the letters to find the names of five of Dennis's comic chums.

1. DAN ON SIDE
2. SLEEP TREND
3. THEN SLUM BULKS
4. REPEATED SAND
5. TAKES BRITS SHED

ANSWER

1. DEAN'S DINO 2. LES PRETEND
3. THE NUMBSKULLS, 4. DESPERATE DAN
5. BASH STREET KIDS.

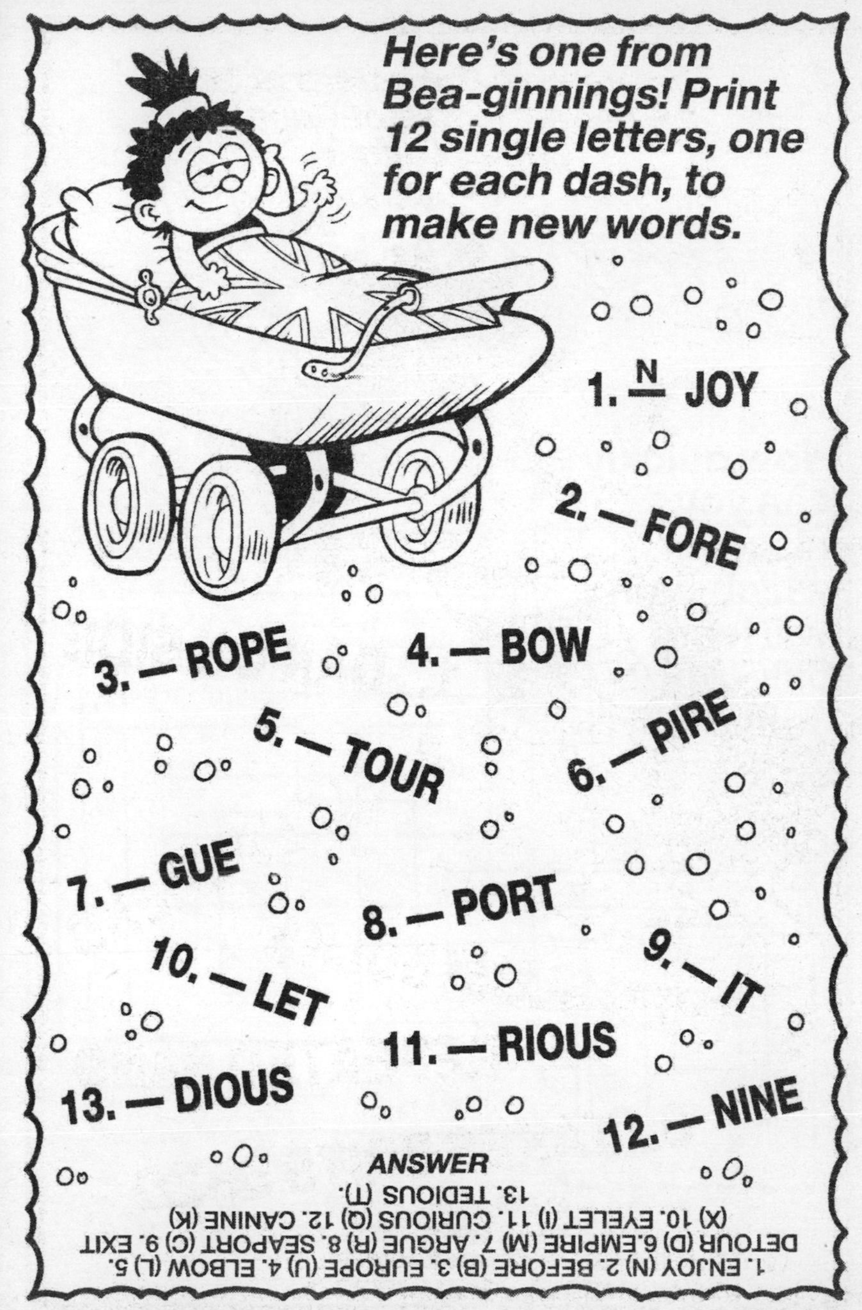

Here's one from Bea-ginnings! Print 12 single letters, one for each dash, to make new words.
1. N JOY
2. — FORE
3. — ROPE
4. — BOW
5. — TOUR
6. — PIRE
7. — GUE
8. — PORT
9. — IT
10. — LET
11. — RIOUS
12. — NINE
13. — DIOUS
ANSWER
1. ENJOY (N) 2. BEFORE (B) 3. EUROPE (U) 4. ELBOW (L) 5. DETOUR (D) 6.EMPIRE (M) 7. ARGUE (R) 8. SEAPORT (C) 9. EXIT (X) 10. EYELET (I) 11. CURIOUS (Q) 12. CANINE (K) 13. TEDIOUS (T).

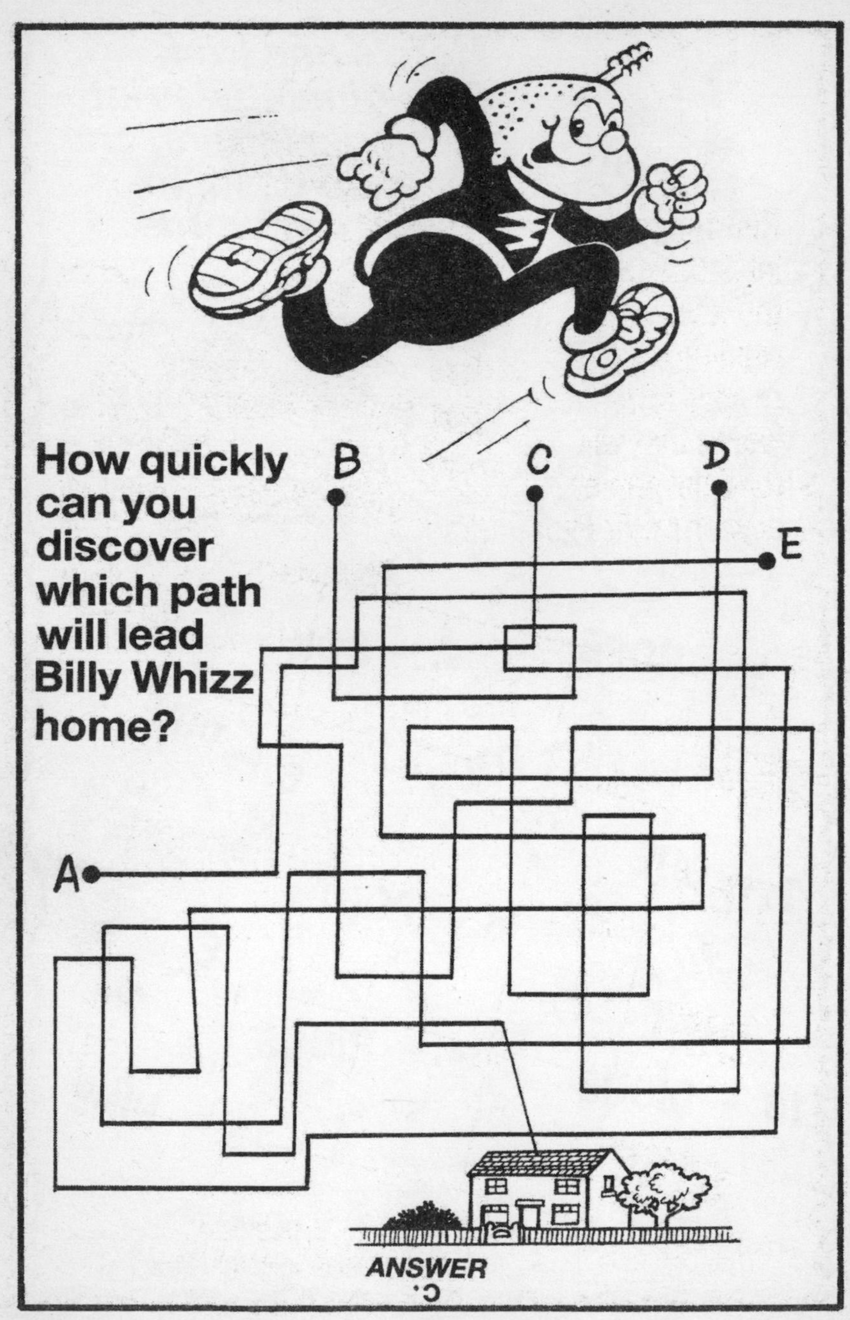
How quickly can you discover which path will lead Billy Whizz home?
B
C
D
E
A
ANSWER
C.

Rearrange the letters in each of the four words, reading across, to spell four words that will read the same across and down.
PEST
TIED
DIET
STEP
ANSWER
Step, tide, edit, pets.

C
S
A
A
Juggle these letters
to spell performers
we often see at the
circus.
T
O
B
R
ANSWER
Acrobats.

*Change **POOR** to **RICH** in eight jumps. Replace one letter to form another word in making each move.*

POOR

1 ____________________

2 ____________________

3 ____________________

4 ____________________

5 ____________________

6 ____________________

7 ____________________

RICH

ANSWER

Here is one correct solution — poor, pool, poll, pole, pale, pace, race, rice, rich.

The cans are piled high, waiting to be knocked down. Using the clues, can you work out the letters which fit in the cans to make a word pyramid? Each word is the same as the last one, plus one letter and we've done the first to start you off.

1. Me. 2. Not out.
3. Writing liquid.
4. Skating area.
5. Thirst quencher.

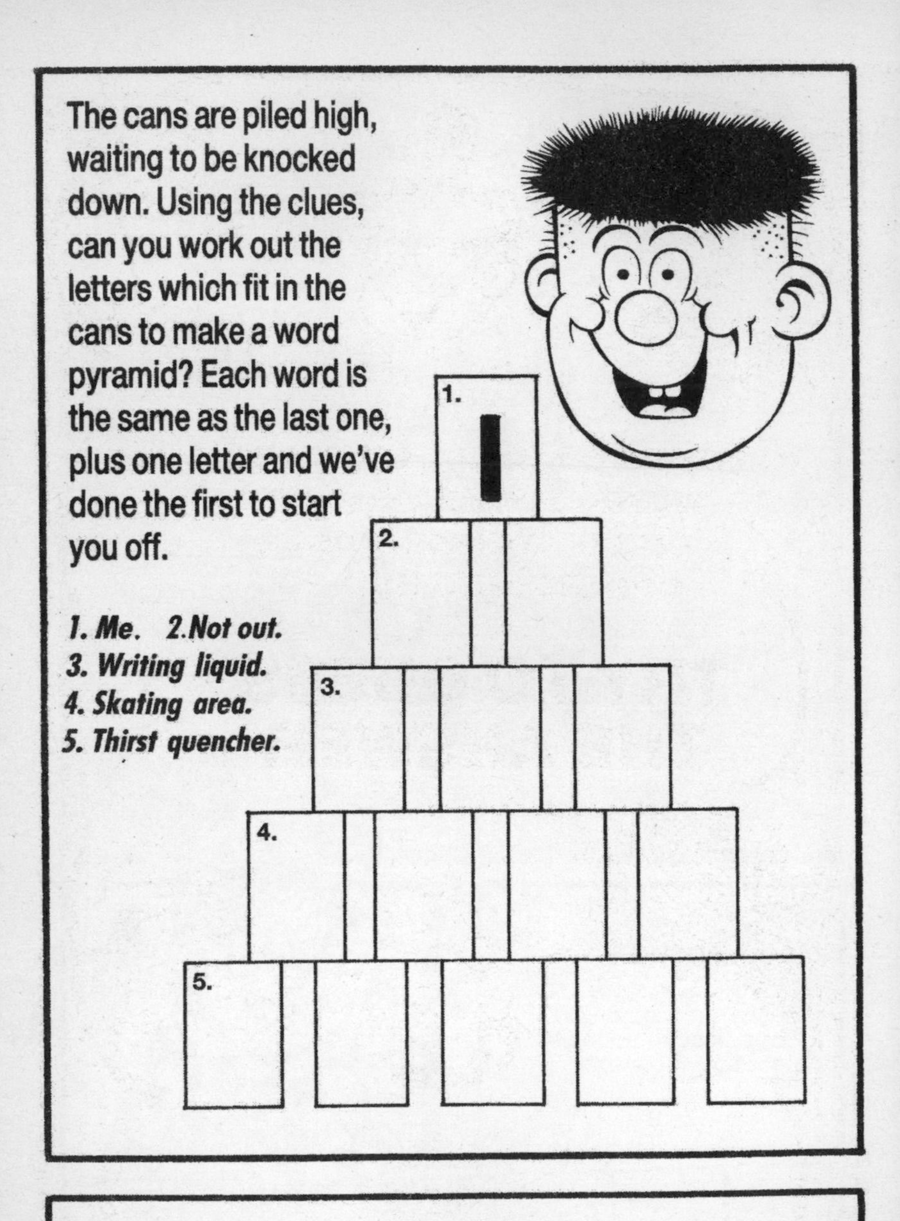

ANSWER

1. I. 2. In. 3. Ink, 4. Rink, 5. Drink.

Take one letter from each word in order, to spell one of these famous character's names.
TRY TO GUESS THE ANSWER
ANSWER
ROGER

Copy this picture of Minnie in the empty grid by making your lines cut through the boxes in exactly the same positions as they do in the originals.

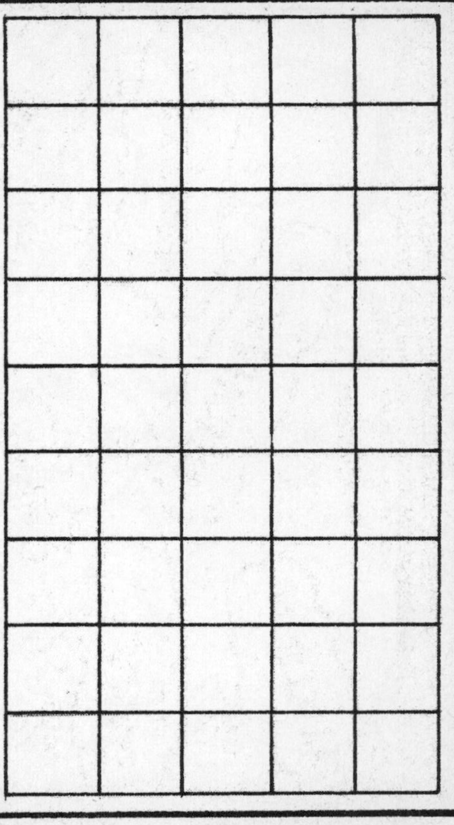

Unscramble each group of letters to spell 10 bodies of WATER.
1. LOPO
2. KALE
3. BOOKR
4. CANOE
5. GOALON
6. TLINE
7. LANAC
8. SETRAM
9. LEAHCNN
10. STATRI
ANSWER
1. Pool. 2. Lake. 3. Brook. 4. Ocean.
5. Lagoon. 6. Inlet. 7. Canal. 8. Stream.
9. Channel. 10. Strait.

Blinky is always getting lost. See if you can help him change LOSE to FIND in seven steps by changing one letter each time.

LOSE

______

______

______

______

______

______

FIND

ANSWER

LOSS, MOSS, MOST, MIST, MINT, MIND, FIND.

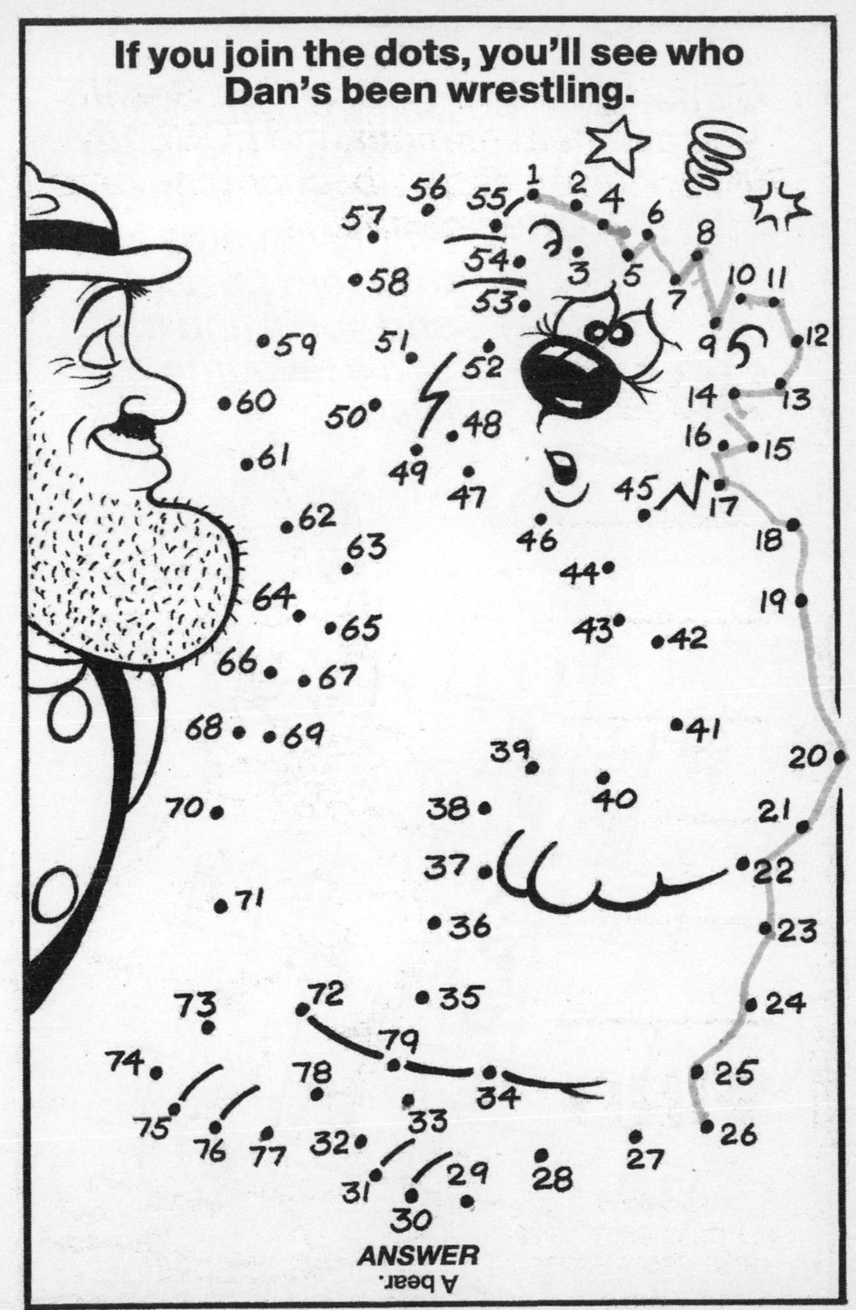
If you join the dots, you'll see who Dan's been wrestling.
ANSWER
A bear.

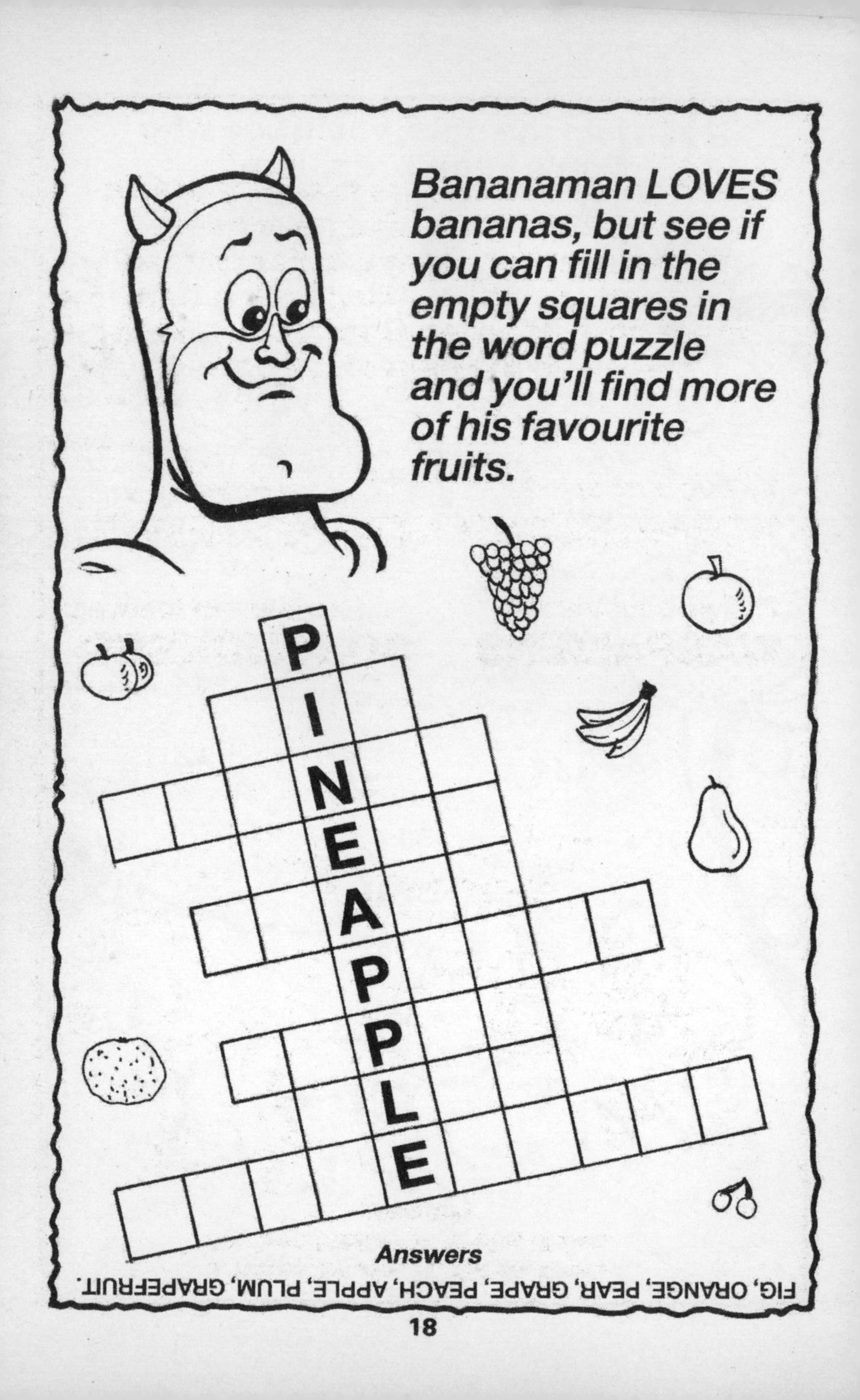
Bananaman LOVES bananas, but see if you can fill in the empty squares in the word puzzle and you'll find more of his favourite fruits.
PINEAPPLE
Answers
FIG, ORANGE, PEAR, GRAPE, PEACH, APPLE, PLUM, GRAPEFRUIT.

Each group of letters is made up of two five-letter words that have been mixed together. Both words still read from left to right, with all their letters in the correct order. Can you separate them with the help of the clues?

1. Two farm animals
HOSHREESEP

2. Two countries
WASPALIENS

3. Two colours
GWREHIETNE

4. Two items of footwear
SOSCHOKSES

ANSWER

1. Horse, Sheep 2. Wales, Spain
3. Green, White 4. Socks, Shoes.

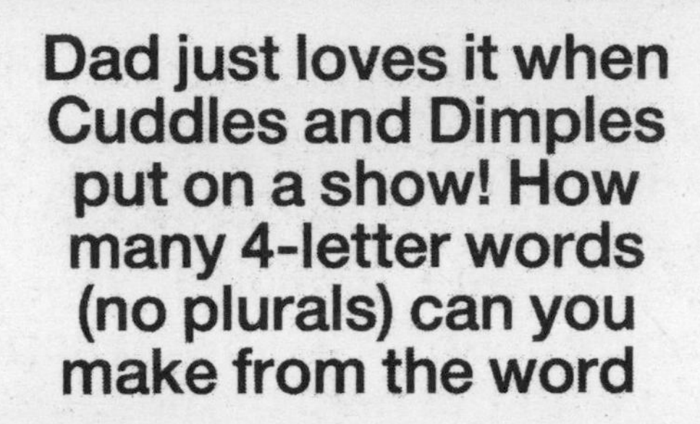

Dad just loves it when Cuddles and Dimples put on a show! How many 4-letter words (no plurals) can you make from the word

ENTERTAINMENT

ANSWER

MINT, MINE, METEOR, MART, MATTER, RANT, RETAIN, RENT, REMAIN, ENTER, NAME, NINE, NEAR, NATTER, NEAT TENT, TEEN, LEER, TART, TIME, TAME, TRAIN, are some.

All these pictures of Plug look equally ugly, but can you spot two which are exactly the same?
1.
2.
3.
4.
5.
ANSWER
Nos. 2 and 5.

Help Ballboy rearrange the jumbled up letters to spell 6 things you might find on a football pitch.
OLAG
LEHISWT
ALBL
ETN
EEFERER
SOPT
ANSWER
GOAL, WHISTLE, BALL,
NET, REFEREE, POST.

Spring into action and solve the clues to find four-letter words which can be made from any of the letters in SPRING!

1. **Piece of jewellery worn on the finger** \- - - -
2. **Big smile** \- - - -
3. **Go round and round** \- - - -
4. **Make music with your voice** \- - - -
5. **Metal fasteners** \- - - -
6. **Hold very tight** \- - - -

ANSWER

1. Ring, 2. Grin, 3. Spin, 4. Sing, 5. Pins, 6. Grip.

Start from certain letters and move from square to square in any direction to spell the names of at least 14 fish.

H	K	I	P	O	N	O
E	C	R	E	B	L	M
A	O	D	A	H	A	I
R	U	D	T	S	B	E
T	A	Y	S	U	E	L

ANSWER

Bass, Cod, Eel, Haddock, Halibut, Perch, Pike, Ray, Roach, Salmon, Shad, Shark, Tarpon, Trout.

Here are two pictures of Roger's bedroom. The first shows it in its usual state, and the second is after his mum's made him tidy it! Nine things have been put back on the shelf, but one thing has gone missing. Can you say what it is?
JIGSAW
JIGSAW
ANSWER
The baseball cap.

Try to think of 8 animals that will rhyme with these 8 words.
CHAIR
HEATER
CAKE
COAL
WAIL
BOAT
HOUSE
RULE
ANSWER
BEAR, CHEETAH, SNAKE, MOLE,
SNAIL, GOAT, MOUSE, MULE.

Use up all the letters in each group to spell two words that sound exactly the same but have different meanings.
1. EEEHHI RRTT
2. AAEEG RRTTG
3. CEEEEN NSS
4. DDOO OLUWW
5. EGHII RRTTW
ANSWER
1. Their and there. 2. Grate and great. 3. Seen and scene.
4. Wood and would. 5. Write and right.

It's Fatty's birthday. To find out what he's wanting for tea, shade in all the boxes that have an even number.

2 T	7 A	46 R	39 B	17 I	64 C	82 O	51 G
37 C	18 L	41 R	9 E	20 T	13 A	56 R	71 M
41 S	20 A	3 P	61 O	12 L	85 N	31 G	97 E
26 S	83 C	16 R	57 A	62 N	23 K	74 L	95 E

ANSWER

A big cream sponge cake.

Change one letter in each word to spell a bird.
1. HARK
2. DOME
3. BROW
4. LARD
5. FERN
ANSWER
1. Hawk. 2. Dove. 3. Crow. 4. Lark. 5. Tern.

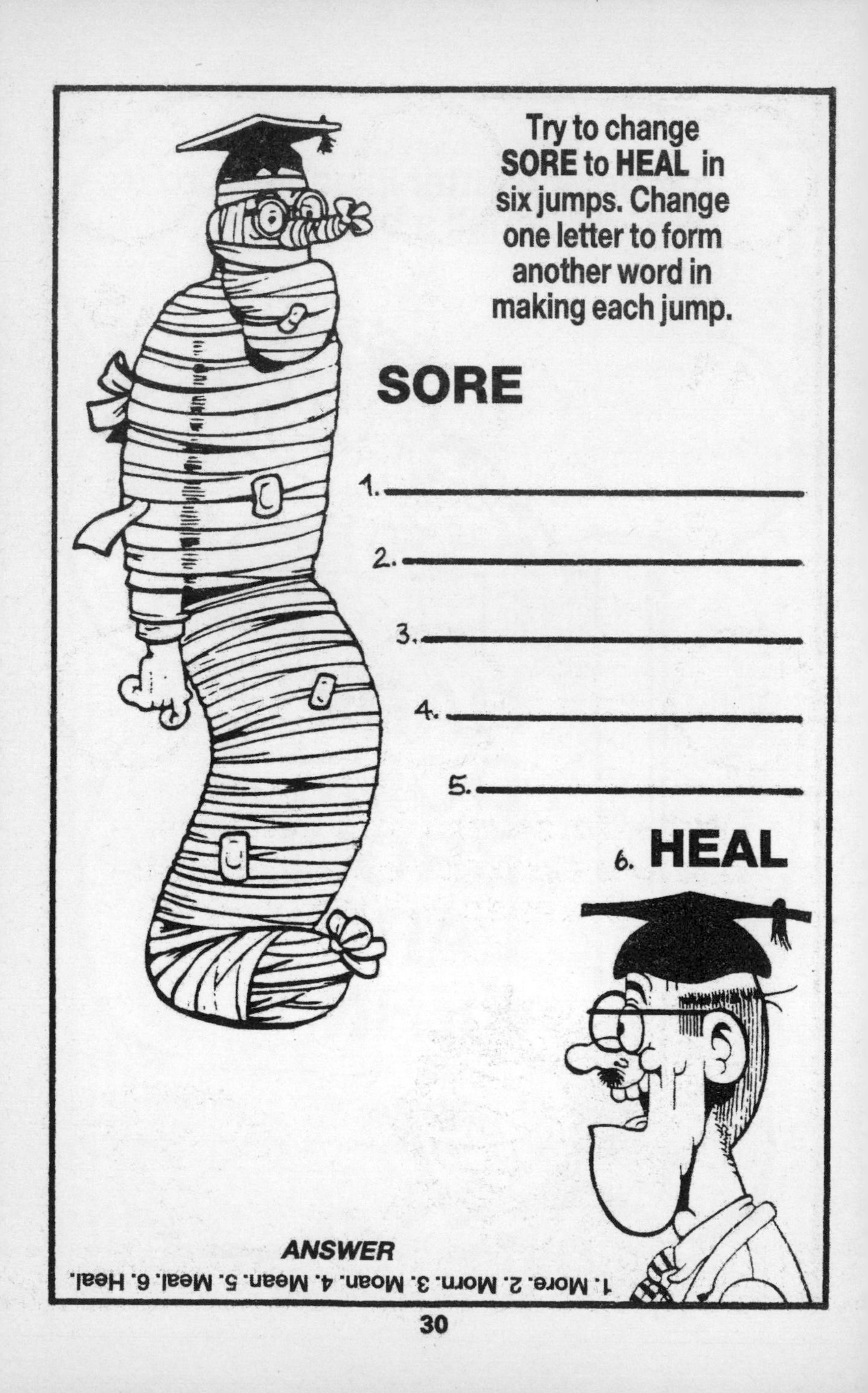

Try to change **SORE to HEAL** in six jumps. Change one letter to form another word in making each jump.

SORE

1. __________

2. __________

3. __________

4. __________

5. __________

6. **HEAL**

ANSWER

1. More. 2. Morn. 3. Moan. 4. Mean. 5. Meal. 6. Heal.

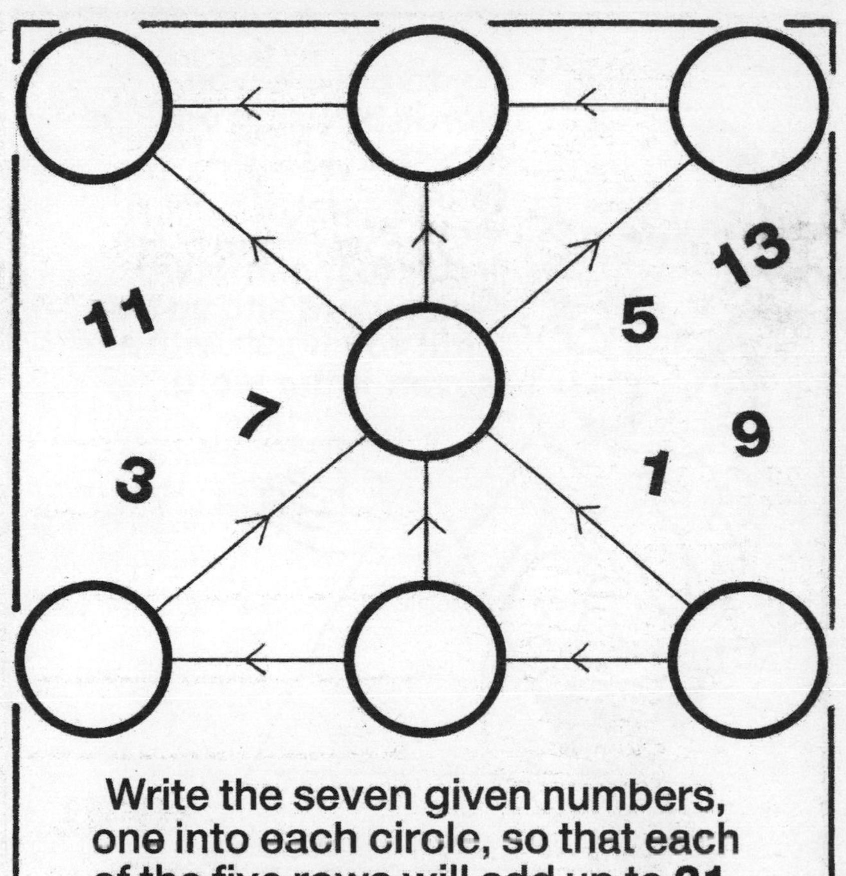

Write the seven given numbers, one into each circle, so that each of the five rows will add up to **21.**

Try to build seven words by using only the letters in LET PART. Start with a one-letter word and add another letter to make a two letter word and so on until you finish with a seven-letter word.

ANSWER

1. A. 2. AT. 3. ATE. 4. LATE. 5. LATER. 6. LATTER. 7. PLATTER.

Use the given 13 letters as often as you wish to spell 10 fruits in our puzzling fruit salad.

ANSWER

Apple, cherry, grape, lemon, melon, orange, peach, pear, plum and prune.

Six Dennis's! It's more than Walter can stand. Never mind, Walter . . . only one is the real Dennis. All the others are copies and they're all exactly alike. Can you spot the real Dennis?
1.
2.
3.
4.
5.
6.
Answer
No. five

Complete the word grid using all the animals in this list.
CAT
DOG
DEER
GOAT
PONY
HORSE
MOUSE
SHEEP
DONKEY
RABBIT
HEDGEHOG
SQUIRREL
HARE
PIG
ANSWER

Smiffy likes to act the clown, but you can make each of the 3 sides of the clown's hat add to exactly 24 by writing the numbers in the circles.

2·3·4·5·6·7·8·9·10

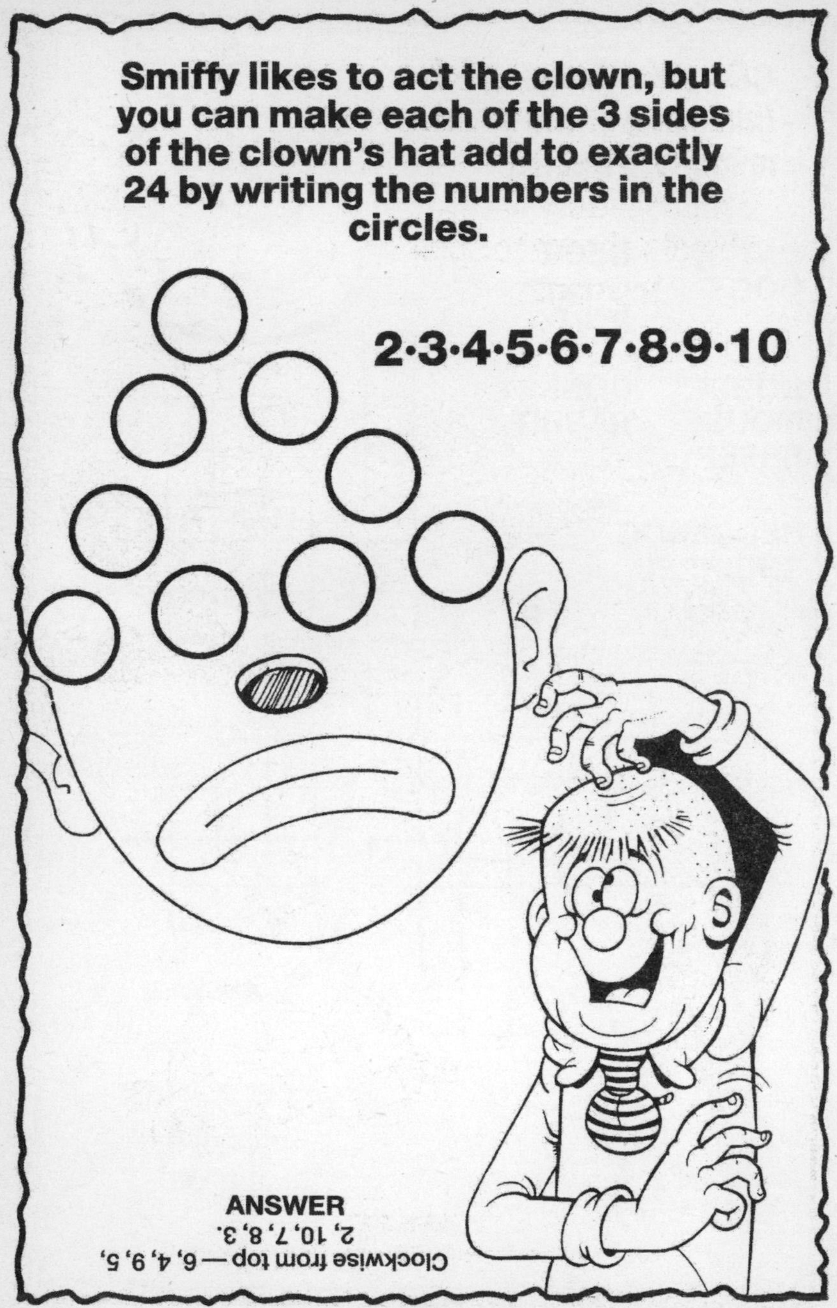

ANSWER

Clockwise from top — 6, 4, 9, 5, 2, 10, 7, 8, 3.

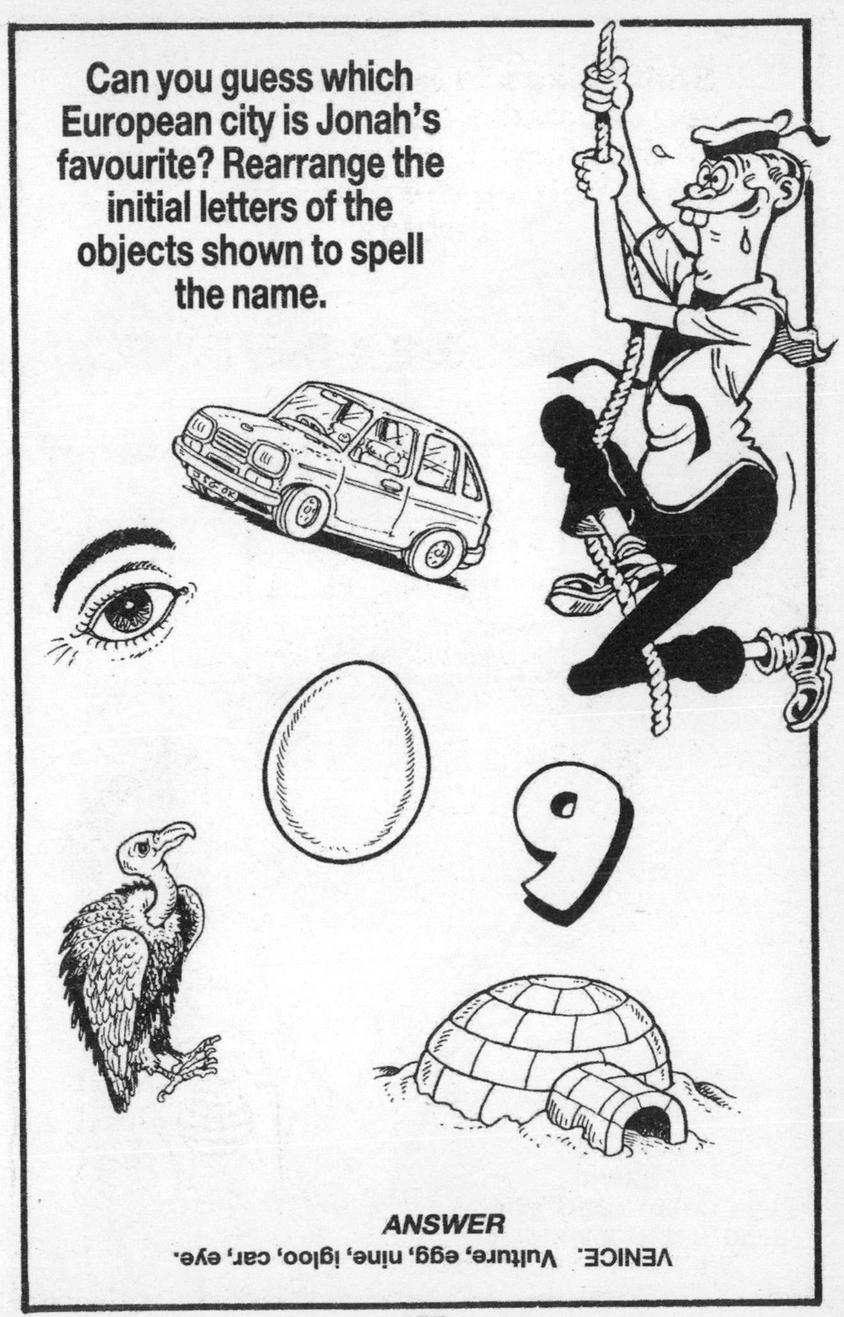
Can you guess which European city is Jonah's favourite? Rearrange the initial letters of the objects shown to spell the name.
ANSWER
VENICE. Vulture, egg, nine, igloo, car, eye.

Teacher's filled in one animal in the puzzle. Now he wants you to fill in the blanks reading downwards to spell the names of 8 more animals.

ANSWER

BAT, PANDA, OTTER, DEER, EAGLE, GOAT, HIPPO, BEAR.

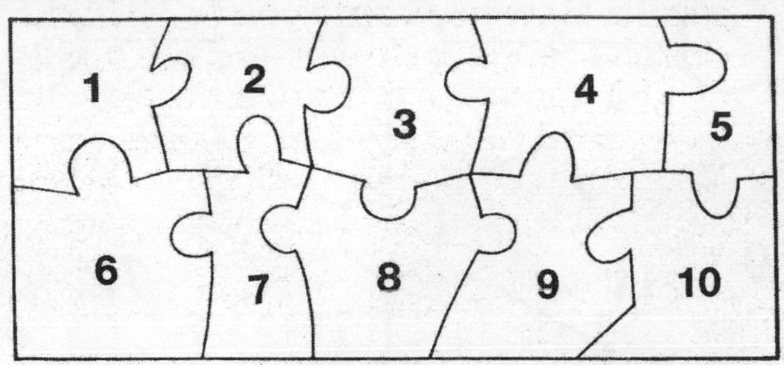

Ten pieces are needed to make the jigsaw. Here they are — but one piece is missing. Which one is it?

ANSWER

No. eight

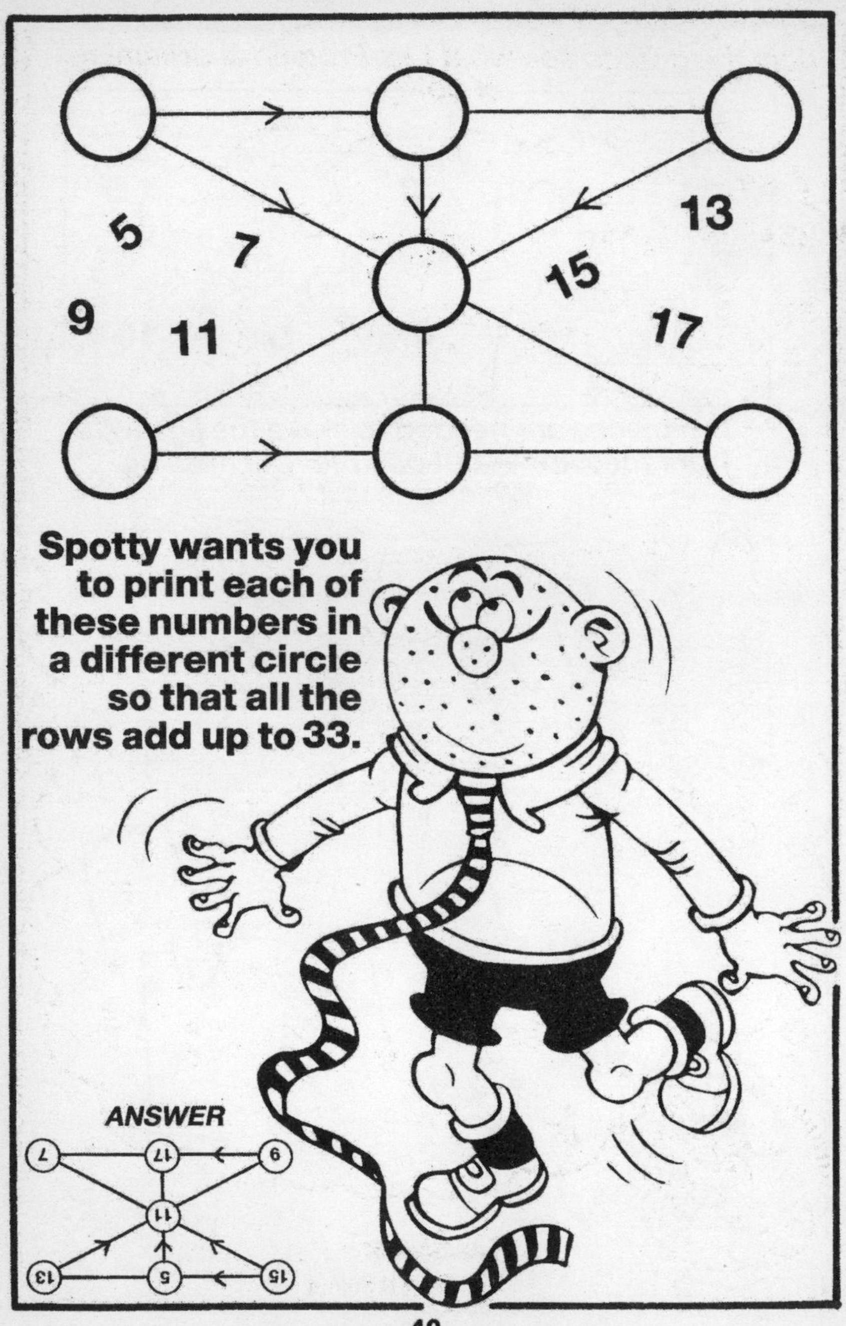
5
7
9
11
13
15
17
Spotty wants you to print each of these numbers in a different circle so that all the rows add up to 33.
ANSWER

Join the dots to see what Les Pretend is dreaming of doing.

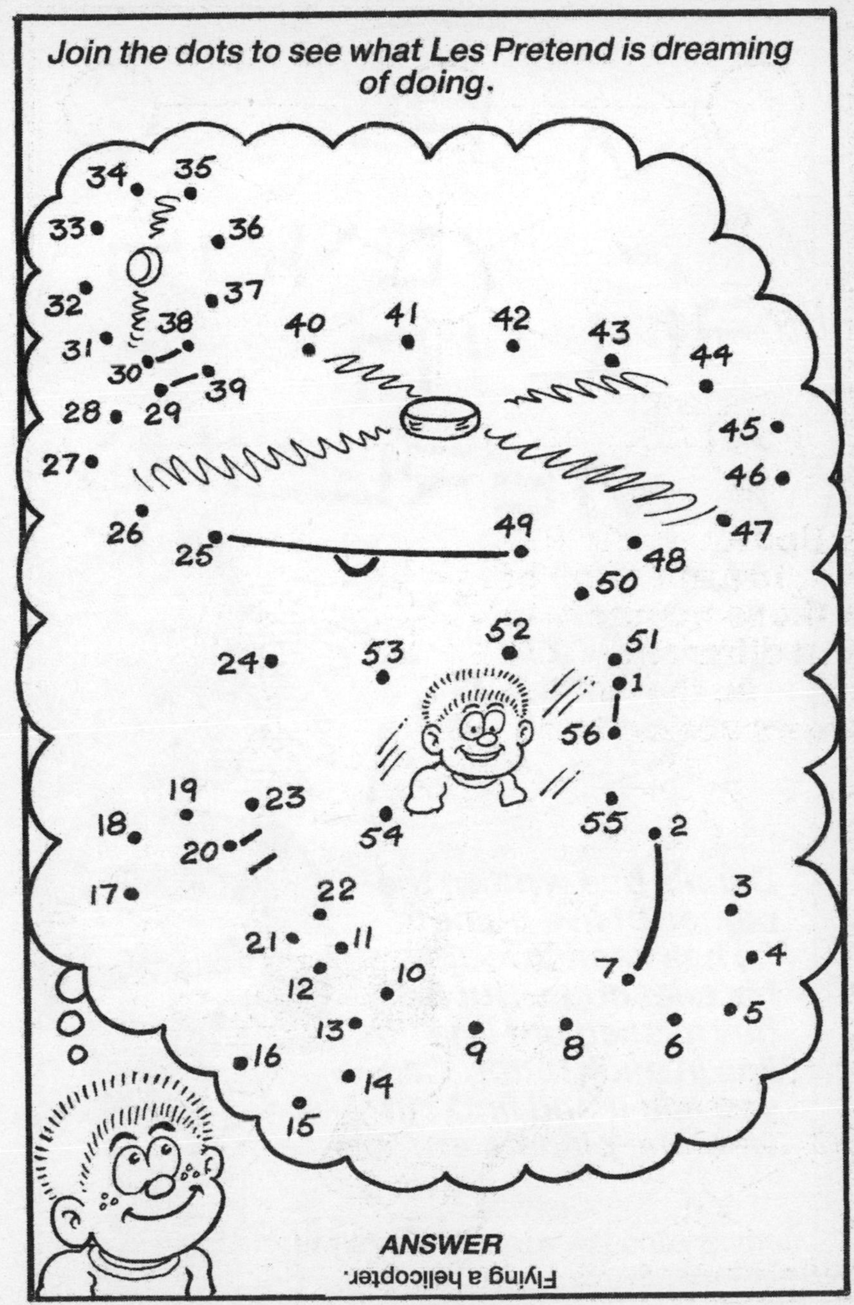

ANSWER

Flying a helicopter.

Dennis has written the names of five planets he has seen through his telescope. But he has missed out one line in each letter. Can you add it and find out what the planets are?

ANSWER

MARS, VENUS, PLUTO, MERCURY, SATURN.

1. I B R O N
2. G O I N P E
Six birds laid these eggs. Unscramble each group of letters to help Smiffy spell their names.
3. N I C E P A L
4. G I L R S T A N
5. T I S H C O R
6. M A I G N L F O
ANSWER
1. Robin. 2. Pigeon. 3. Pelican. 4. Starling. 5. Ostrich. 6 Flamingo.

Print one letter over each dash to spell five creatures.
1. — O — SE
2. — O — SE
3. — O — SE
4. — O — SE
5. — O — SE
ANSWER
1. Horse. 2. Mouse. 3. Moose.
4. Goose. 5. Louse.

Fill in the empty squares to complete words that suit the clues.

MONTH	***M***	***A***	***R***					
COLOUR	***M***	***A***	***R***					
BIRD	***M***	***A***	***R***					
STONE	***M***	***A***	***R***					
WONDER	***M***	***A***	***R***					
FLOWER	***M***	***A***	***R***					
LONG RACE	***M***	***A***	***R***					

ANSWER

March, maroon, martin, marble, marvel, marigold, marathon.

Three four-letter words that are spelled with the same letters are missing from this sentence. Try to fill them in.

ITS - - - - IS LEO AND IT HAS A - - - - LOOK AND A LONG - - - -

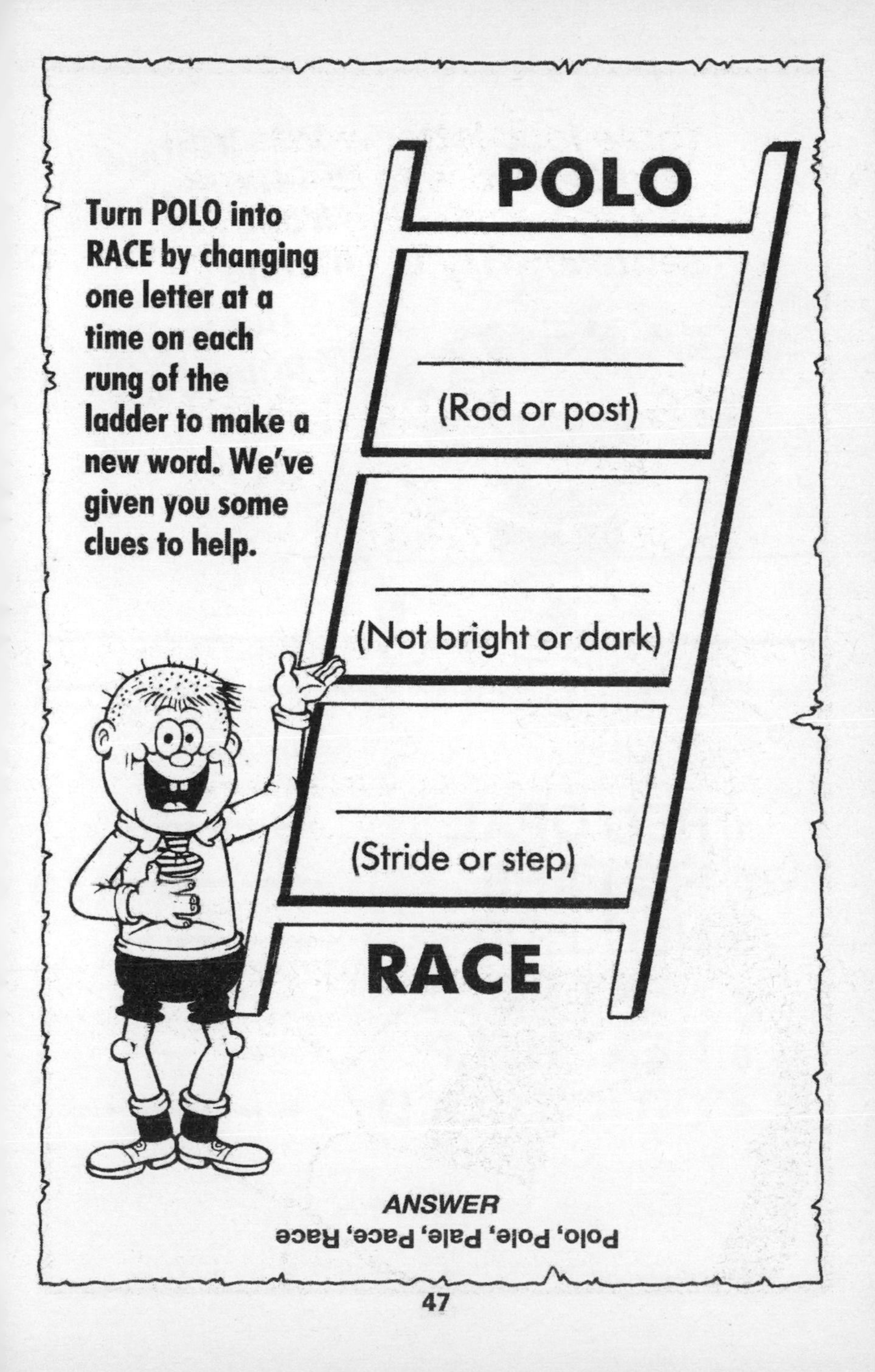
Turn POLO into RACE by changing one letter at a time on each rung of the ladder to make a new word. We've given you some clues to help.
POLO
(Rod or post)
(Not bright or dark)
(Stride or step)
RACE
ANSWER
Polo, Pole, Pale, Pace, Race

1 **RED OPAL** ______

2 **FIG FARE** ______

3 **HEN TRAP** ______

4 **NEAT POLE** ______

5 **NEAT HELP** ______

6 **OR ICE COLD** ______

ANSWER

1. LEOPARD. 2. GIRAFFE 3. PANTHER. 4. ANTELOPE. 5. ELEPHANT. 6. CROCODILE.

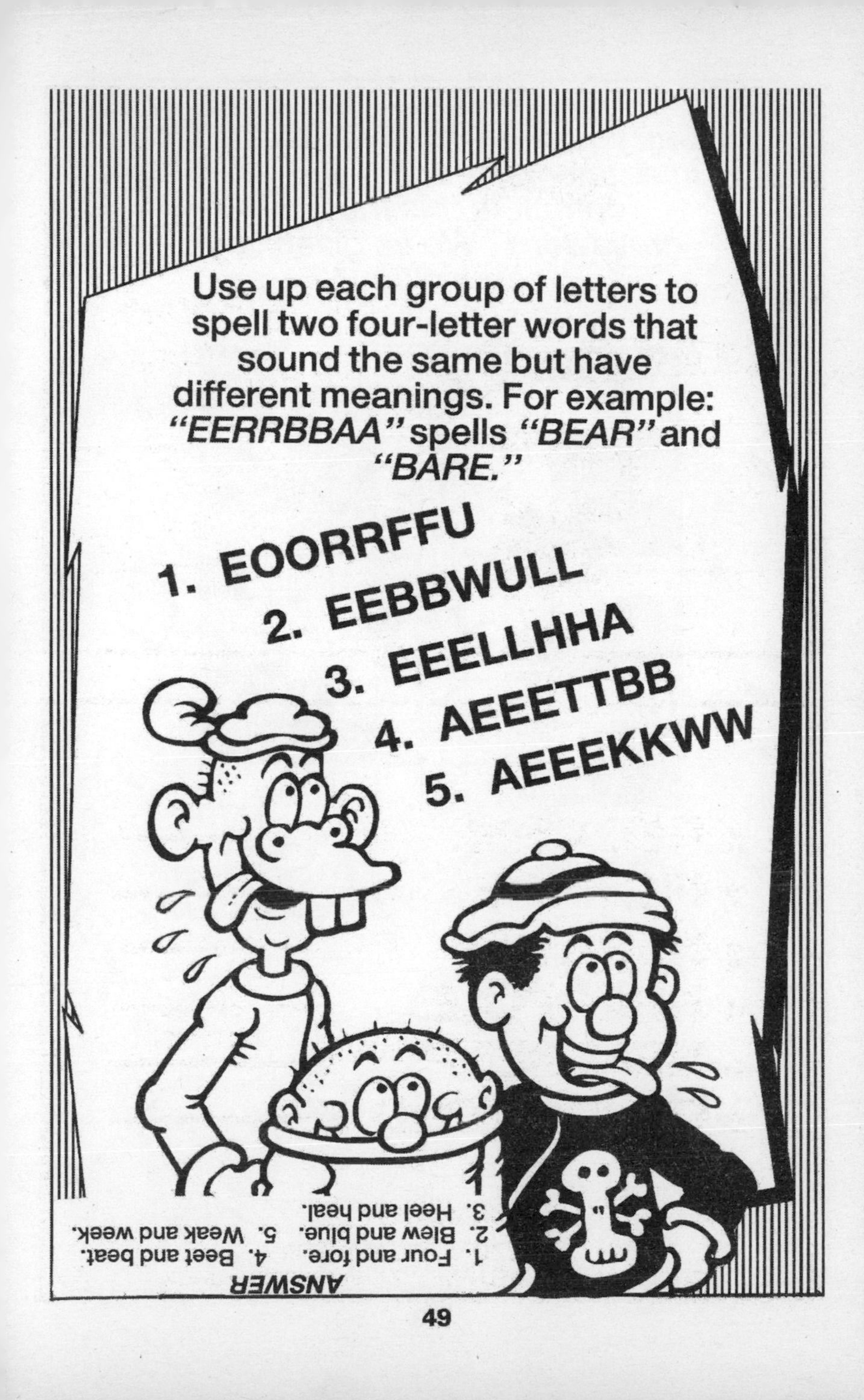
Use up each group of letters to spell two four-letter words that sound the same but have different meanings. For example: "EERRBBAA" spells "BEAR" and "BARE."
1. EOORRFFU
2. EEBBWULL
3. EEELLHHA
4. AEEETTBB
5. AEEEKKWW
ANSWER
1. Four and fore.
2. Blew and blue.
3. Heel and heal.
4. Beet and beat.
5. Weak and week.

Can you write in eleven musical instruments, reading across, to complete this musical crossword? We've given you some clues.
INSTRUMENTS
M
C
C
ANSWER
GUITAR, PIANO, BASS, LUTE, TRUMPET, TAMBOURINE, DRUM, CELLO, CLARINET, FLUTE, CASTANET.

Use all of the nineteen letters shown below to spell well-known words. Here are the clues.

1. The tallest living animal. ____________________

2. A man-eating fish. ____________________

3. A three-letter beverage. ____________________

4. A four-letter vegetable. ____________________

ANSWER

1. Giraffe. 2. Shark. 3. Tea. 4. Beet.

A wordsquare reads the same across and down. Use the words below to make two wordsquares which each contain the word RIDE.

ADDS
BEST
DEAR
EARS
GRAB
IDEA
RIDE
RIDE

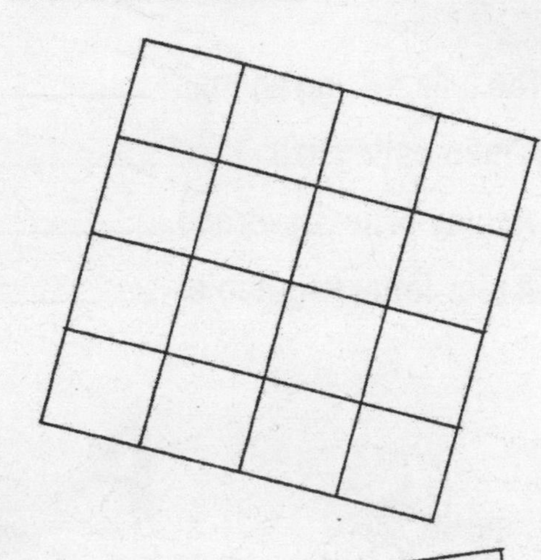

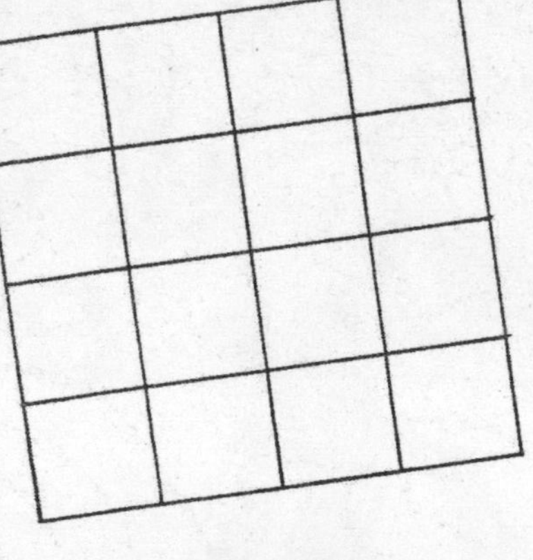

ANSWER (printed upside down)

R	I	D	E
I	D	E	A
D	E	A	R
E	A	R	S

G	R	A	B
R	I	D	E
A	D	D	S
B	E	S	T

Ulp! Jonah's in deep water again. Follow the maze to see what's going to happen to him.

What's the magician about to produce from his hat? Look for what's not there and then you'll see it . . . if you see what we mean! Take the letters of the alphabet that do NOT appear on the hat and use them to discover the mystery object.
X
K
P
F
Q
G
J
W
L
N
A
S
H
T
R
U
I
Z
C
B
M
Y
ANSWER
Dove

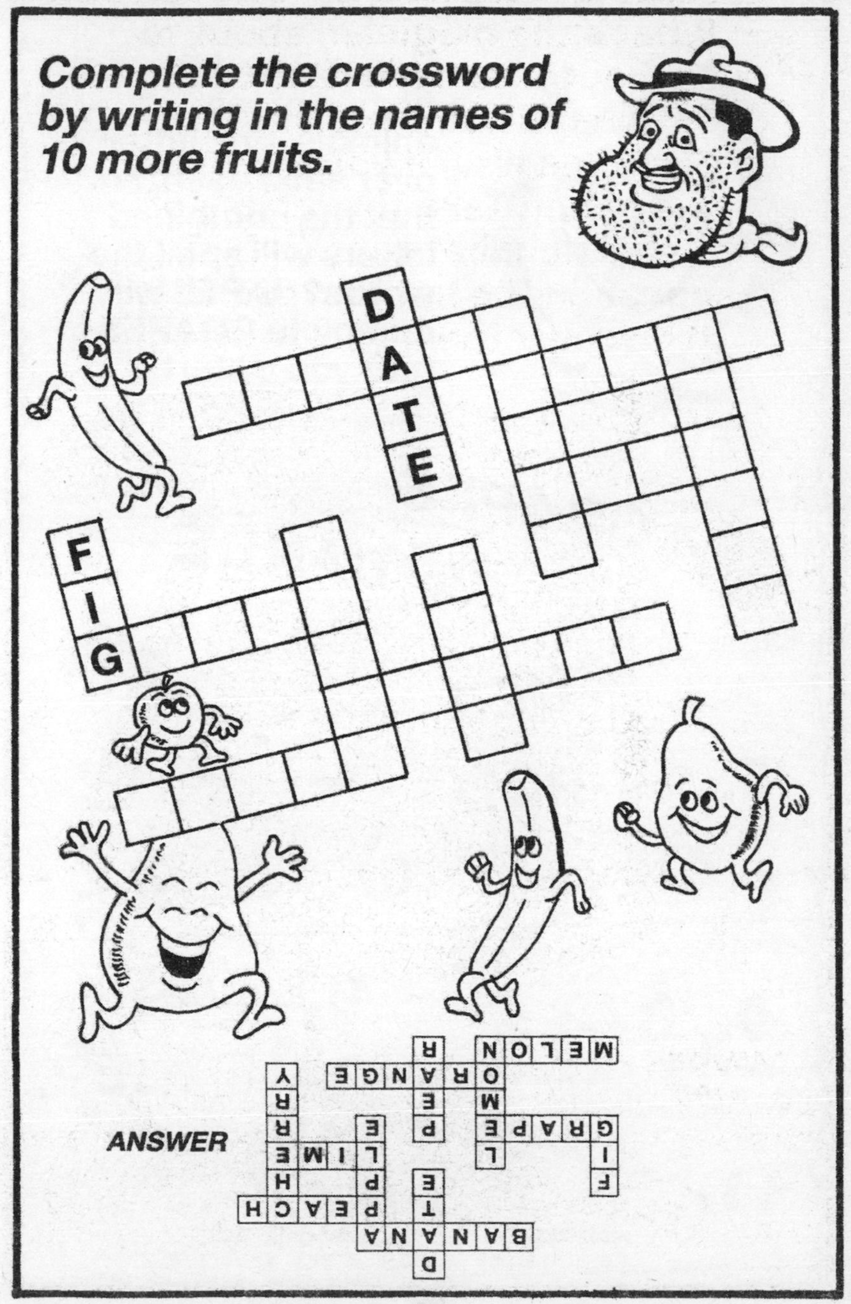
Complete the crossword
by writing in the names of
10 more fruits.
DATE
FIG
ANSWER

Can you add the names of ten animals, one letter over each dash, so that the combined letters will spell the words? "APE" will complete GRAPES to give you a start.

1. GR<u>APES</u>

2. DANDE----

3. ---CHER

4. ---ARD

5. ---ROD

6. ----GER

7. ----EE

8. ---S

9. B--ES

10. ---ES

11. ----DED

ANSWER

2. Lion. 3. Cat. 4. Cow. 5. Ram. 6. Stag.
7. Goat. 8. Doe. 9. Ox. 10. Rat. 11. Bear.

Copy this picture of Dan in the empty grid by making your lines cut through the boxes in exactly the same positions as they do in the originals.

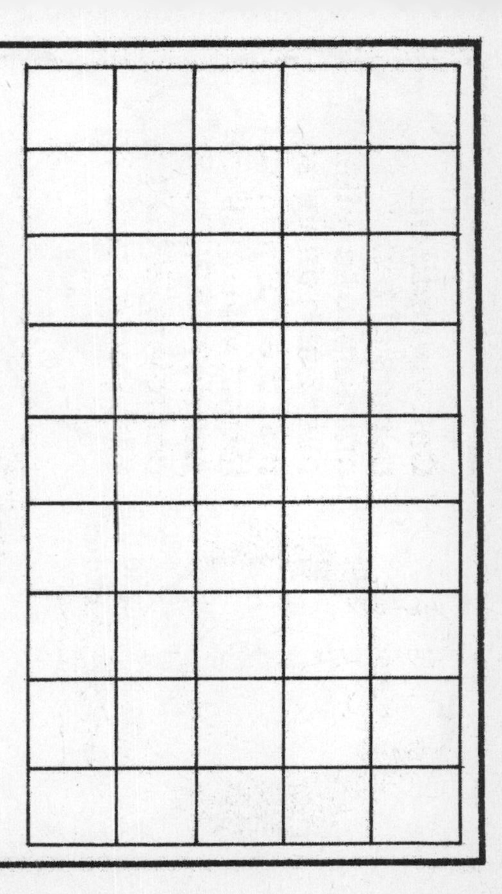

Seven incomplete words meaning "HAPPY" are listed below. Can you print a letter over each dash to make the words?
1. M — — R —
2. — O — F — L
3. G — A —
4. — A —
5. — O — L —
6. — H — — R — — —
7. — LE — — U —
ANSWER
1. Merry. 2. Joyful. 3. Glad. 4. Gay.
5. Jolly. 6. Cheerful. 7. Gleeful.

Help Little Plum rearrange the initials of these five pictures to spell a fruit, then juggle them again to spell another fruit.

ANSWER

Octopus, Lamp, Monkey, Eel and Nail can spell MELON and then LEMON.

Let the Bash Street Kids help you spell out the names of four animals. Each different Kid stands for a different letter of the alphabet. Start with . . .

Danny — C
Toots — A
Sydney — T.

1. ___ ___ ___

2. ___ ___ ___ ___ ___

3. ___ ___ ___

4. ___ ___ ___ ___ ___

ANSWER

1. Cat 2. Camel 3. Ape 4. Llama

Can you match the book titles to their amazing authors?

TITLES

1. On The Beach
2. At The South Pole
3. A Cliff Top Tragedy
4. How To Feed A Dog
5. The Millionaire

BY

a) Nora Bone
b) Ivor Fortune
c) C. Shaw
d) Eileen Dover
e) Ann Tarctic

ANSWER

1c), 2e), 3d), 4a), 5b).

Try to spell at least 10 words that will rhyme with ***"SING"***. Start from certain letters in the boxes and move to the next letter in any direction.
C L S T
F N I R
P I G W
K H T S
ANSWER
Cling, fling, king, ling, ping, ring, sing, sling, string, swing, thing, wing and wring are 13.

Follow the paths the paint tubes take to each numbered area, saying which two paints meet there, and what colour they'll make when mixed together.

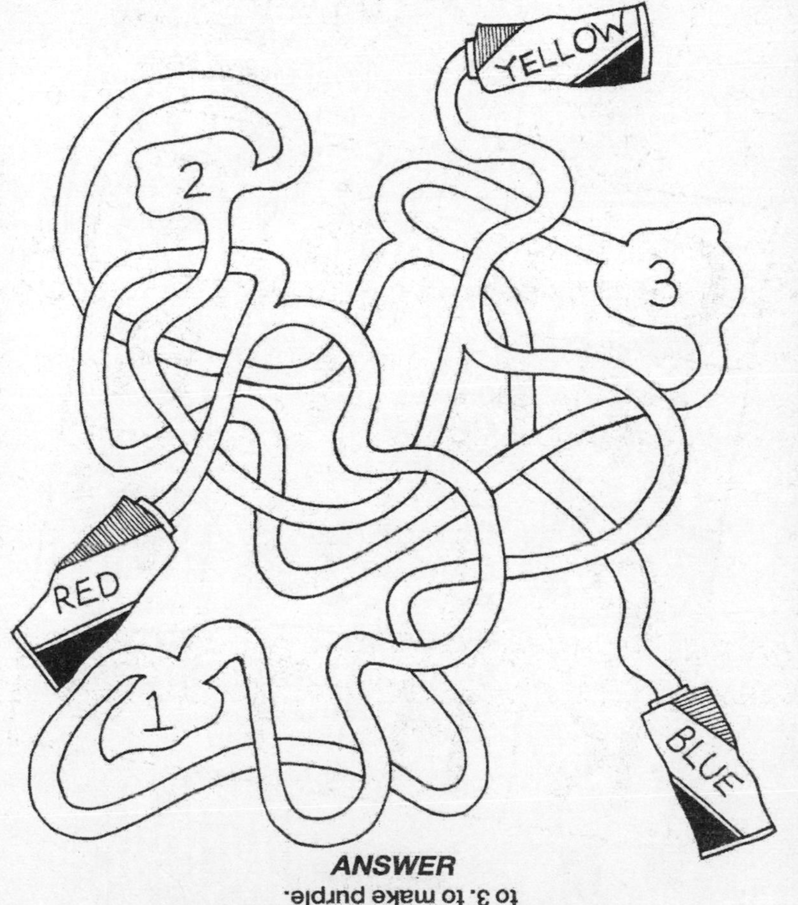

ANSWER

Red and yellow lead to 1. to make orange. Blue and yellow lead to 2. to make green. Blue and red lead to 3. to make purple.

Can you find all the listed indoor games in this wordsearch? The *Snake* words go down, either straight or diagonally, while the *Ladder* words all go up.

L X L T S A S T S J D T
G L P N Y E D I E X O P
H J A U H L R D L P M G
C P T B X E A D T I I V
O H I Y N R C L T N N S
N G E P T I W Y I G O E
K A N S V A P W K P E L
E M C I S T S I S O S B
R E E O B I N N I N T R
S B U D E L A K A G Z A
A O L U H O P S X R O M
Z Y R L P S D S L T I Y

Snakes
CHESS
CONKERS
DARTS
DOMINOES
GAMEBOY
PATIENCE
PINGPONG
SNAP
TIDDLYWINKS

Ladders
BINGO
CARDS
I-SPY
LUDO
MARBLES
PINBALL
SKITTLES
SOLITAIRE

ANSWER

Three of the Bash Street Kids' friends are visiting with their dogs, but they've got themselves in a bit of a tangle! If you follow the letters on the lead, then you'll discover the name of each dog, and you'll be able to say to whom it belongs, too!
1.
2.
3.
B
G
R
M
M
L
S
E
A
N
L
U
A
Y
O
A.
B.
C.
ANSWER
Child 1 owns dog C, named Sally.
Child 2 owns dog A, named Gemma.
Child 3 owns dog B, named Bruno.

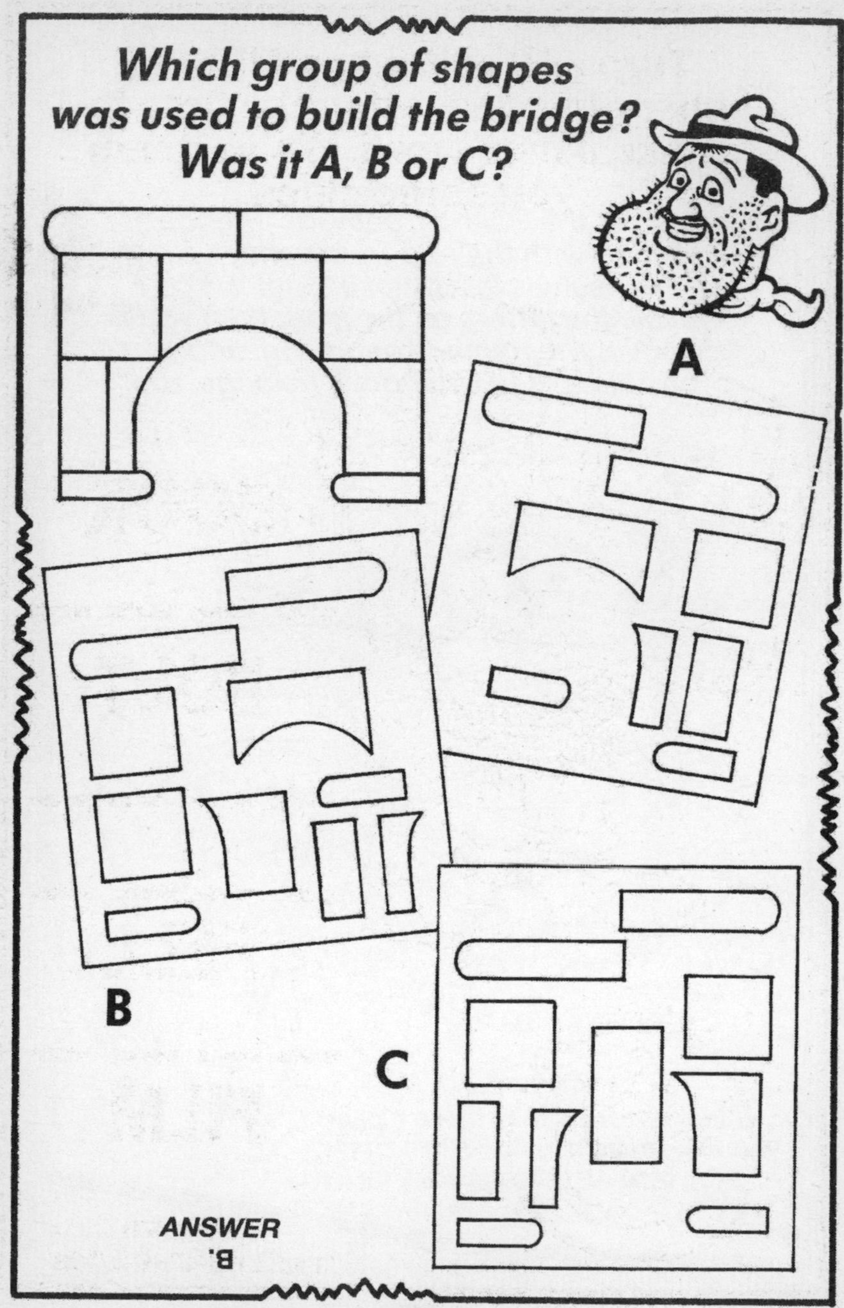
Which group of shapes
was used to build the bridge?
Was it A, B or C?
A
B
C
ANSWER
B.

Turn a BOOK into a FILM by changing one letter at a time to make a new word. We've given you some clues.

BOOK

_ _ _ _

BOLT

_ _ _ _

_ _ _ _

FELL

_ _ _ _

FILM

ANSWER

BOOT, BELT, FELT, FILL.

Up to 5 people can play this game. All you have to do is choose a dog and then trace along the line leading from it. Whoever fetches the ball is the winner.

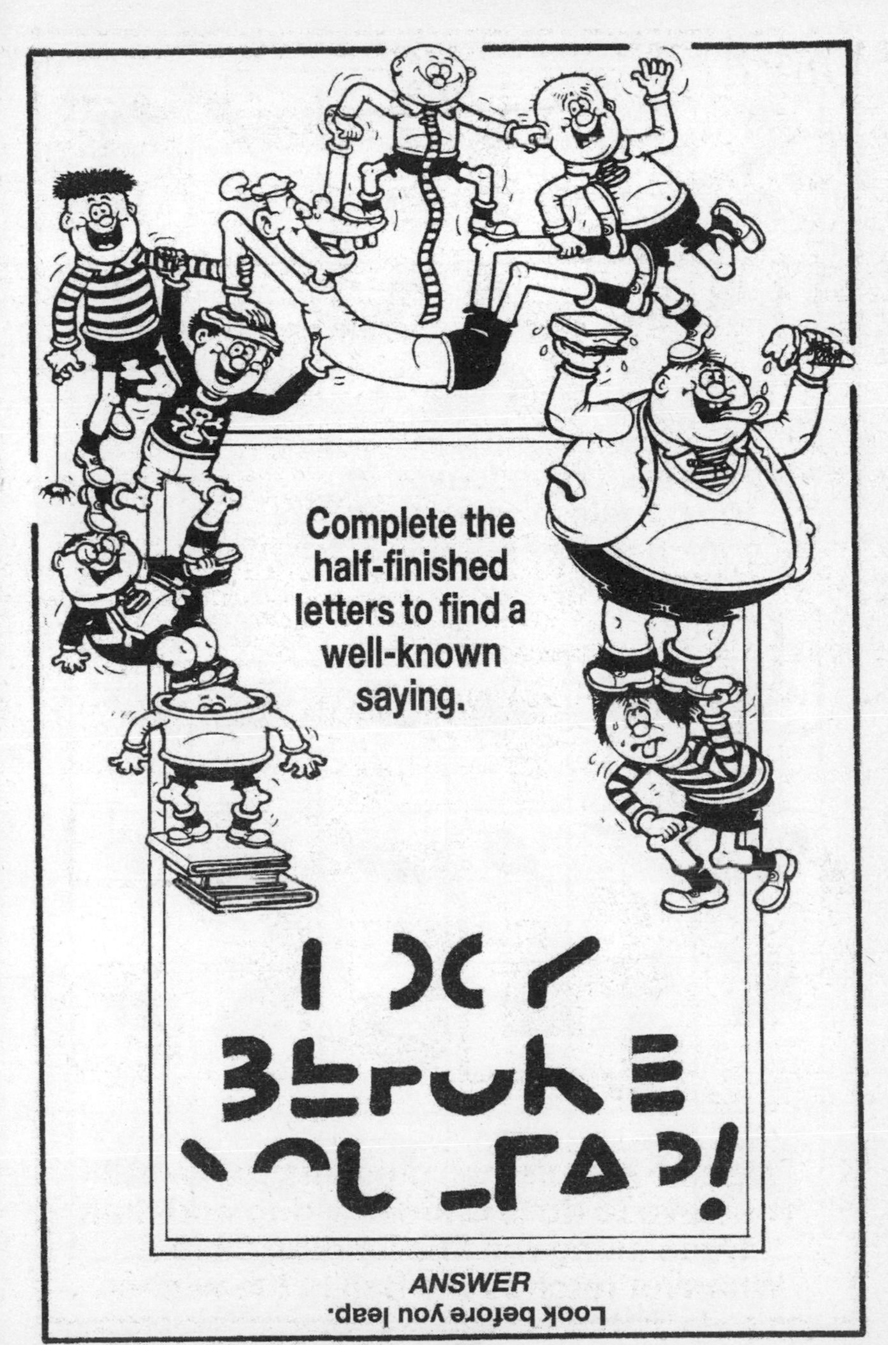

ANSWER

Look before you leap.

ANSWER

WINTER, SPRING, S UMMER, AUTUMN.

No wonder Dan looks puzzled. He's trying to see how many four-lettered words he can make from his name. How many can you make?
DESPERATE DAN
ANSWER
Sped, trap, tend, peer, reed, date, dane, seep, seat, pane, sane, dare, pate, tear, data, send, rate, pend, dear, deep, deer, dart, dean, seed, are some.

Write a different single number in every empty box to make each of the five rows add up to 15.

ANSWER

Top row across — 6, 7, 2.
Bottom row across — 8, 3, 4.

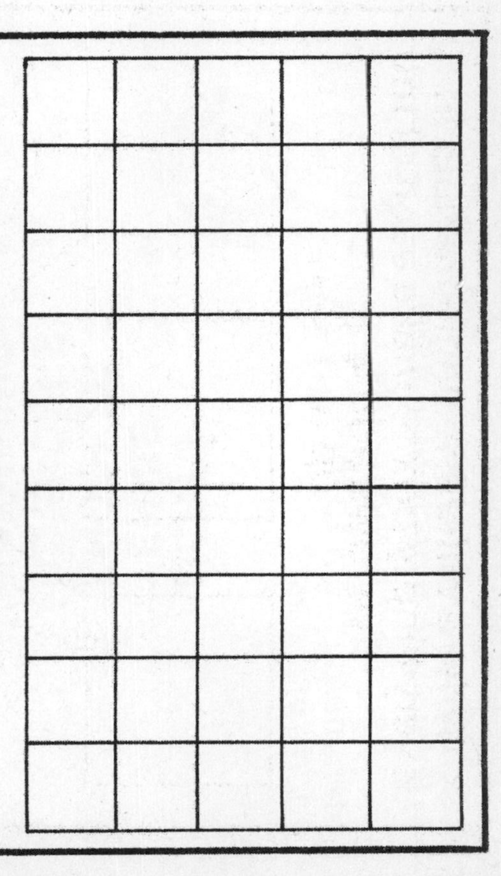

Copy this picture of Little Plum in the empty grid by making your lines cut through the boxes in exactly the same positions as they do in the originals.

Each picture represents a word that is linked with a particular sport. Can you identify the words, then match them to the sports in the list?

DARTS
TENNIS
SNOOKER
ROUNDERS
SWIMMING

ANSWER

Darts — Bull, Tennis — Ace, Snooker — Pocket, Rounders — Bat, Swimming — Butterfly.

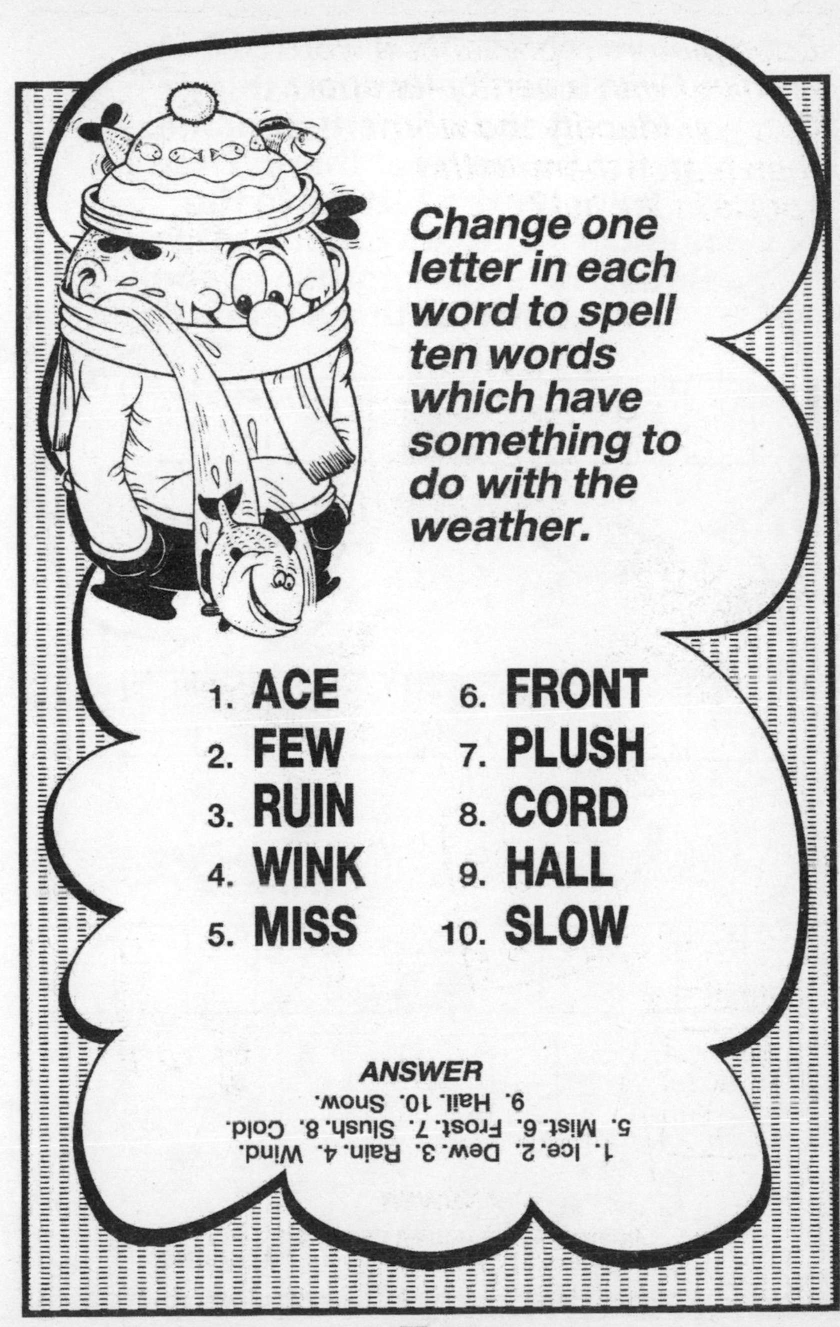

Change one letter in each word to spell ten words which have something to do with the weather.
1. ACE
2. FEW
3. RUIN
4. WINK
5. MISS
6. FRONT
7. PLUSH
8. CORD
9. HALL
10. SLOW
ANSWER
1. Ice. 2. Dew. 3. Rain. 4. Wind.
5. Mist. 6. Frost. 7. Slush. 8. Cold.
9. Hail. 10. Snow.

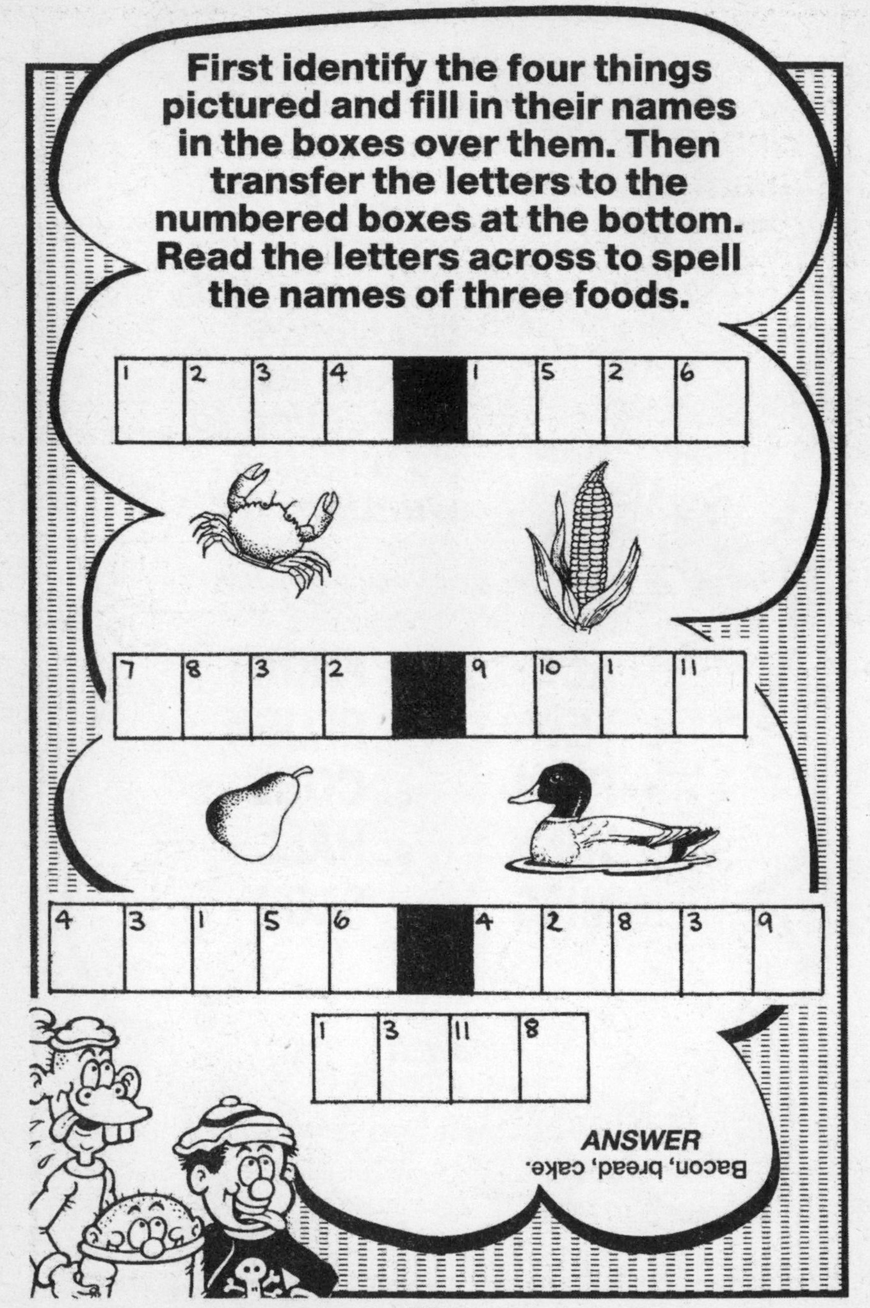
First identify the four things pictured and fill in their names in the boxes over them. Then transfer the letters to the numbered boxes at the bottom. Read the letters across to spell the names of three foods.
1 2 3 4 1 5 2 6
7 8 3 2 9 10 1 11
4 3 1 5 6 4 2 8 3 9
1 3 11 8
ANSWER
Bacon, bread, cake.

Blinky thinks he's
seeing double.
Can you spot six
differences between
these two pictures?
ANSWER

Use the letters below as many times as you wish and try to spell the names of twelve animals.

ANSWER

Cow, sow, cat, dog, rat, goat, ass, steer, deer, stag, doe, ewe.

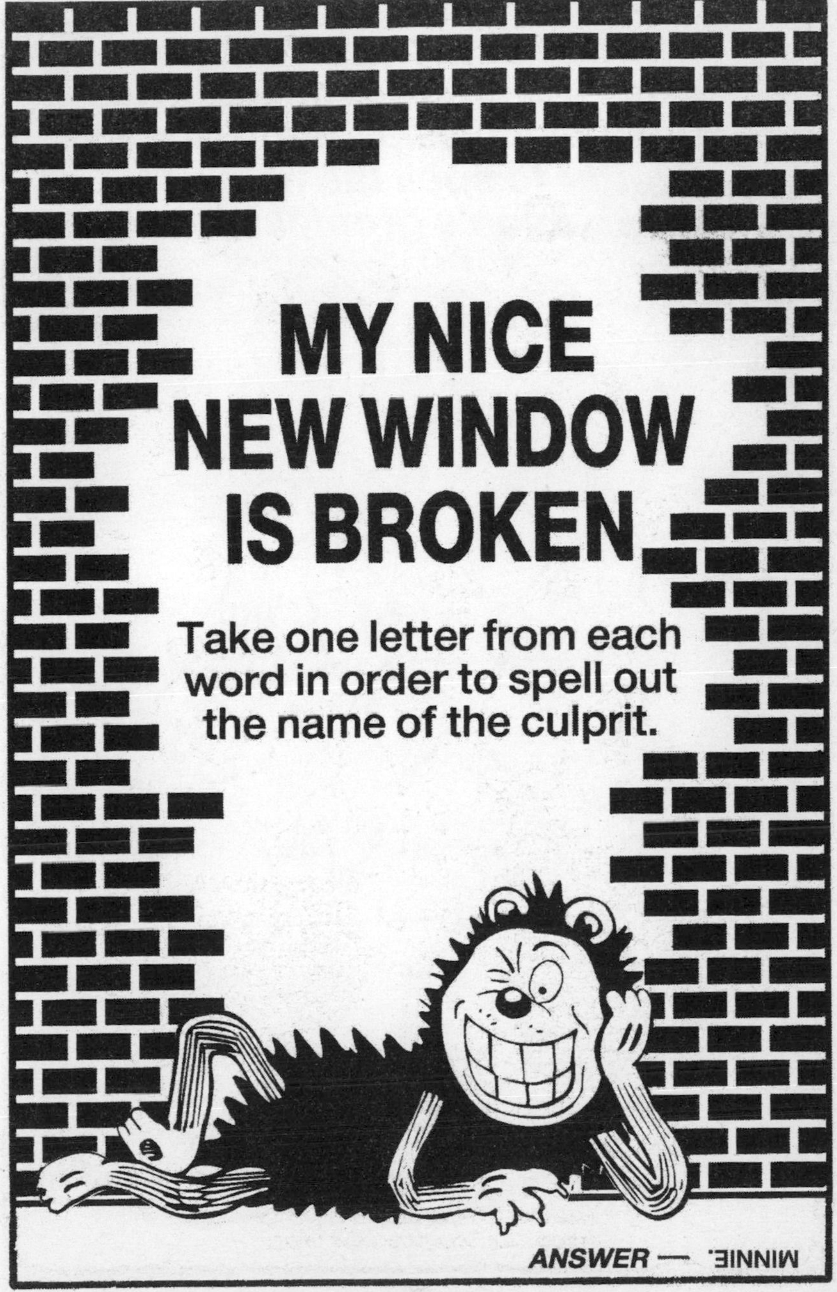
MY NICE NEW WINDOW IS BROKEN
Take one letter from each word in order to spell out the name of the culprit.
ANSWER — MINNIE.

Starting at the letter C, move round the circle in a clockwise direction, missing every second letter to spell the name of Bananaman's greatest enemy.
C B A L P I T G A H I T N
ANSWER
Captain Blight.

SLOW

Billy Whizz can do 0-30 m.p.h. in eight seconds . . . but can you change SLOW to FAST in eight moves? Change one letter to form an other word in making each jump.

1. ____________________
2. ____________________
3. ____________________
4. ____________________
5. ____________________
6. ____________________
7. ____________________
8. **FAST**

ANSWER

1. Flow. 2. Flaw. 3. Flat.
4. Feat. 5. Peat.
6. Pest. 7. Past.
8. Fast.

Cuthbert has to choose a new bear — and of course, just to be fussy, he wants one with black ears, and a bow tie. Its nose must match its ears and he doesn't want a sad bear. He doesn't like spots on bow ties. Can you work out which one he takes?
1.
2.
3.
4.
5.
6.
7.
8.
ANSWER
No. 6.

Here's one from Ballboy. Complete the word puzzle, reading down, by writing in the names of eight more sports.
FOOTBALL
ANSWER

What are these 8 words that start with "SO"? Print a letter over each dash to complete them. The definitions are under the incomplete words.

1. SO _ _
   FLY

2. SO _ _
   COUCH

3. SO _ _
   MELODY

4. SO _ _
   WASHING MATERIAL

5. SO _ _
   SATURATE

6. SO _ _ _ _
   A GAME

7. SO _ _ _
   REGRETFUL

8. SO _ _
   EARTH

ANSWER

1. Soar. 2. Sofa. 3. Song. 4. Soap. 5. Soak. 6. Soccer. 7. Sorry. 8. Soil.

1. ULEFT
2. RENTCO
Unscramble each group of letters to spell 6 musical instruments.
3. URAGIT
4. OLDMANNI
5. PUTMERT
6. LINETCAR
ANSWER
1. Flute. 2. Cornet.
3. Guitar. 4. Mandolin.
5. Trumpet. 6. Clarinet.

Gnasher wants you to guess the names of these six pictures and then rearrange the initials to spell the name of a type of dog.

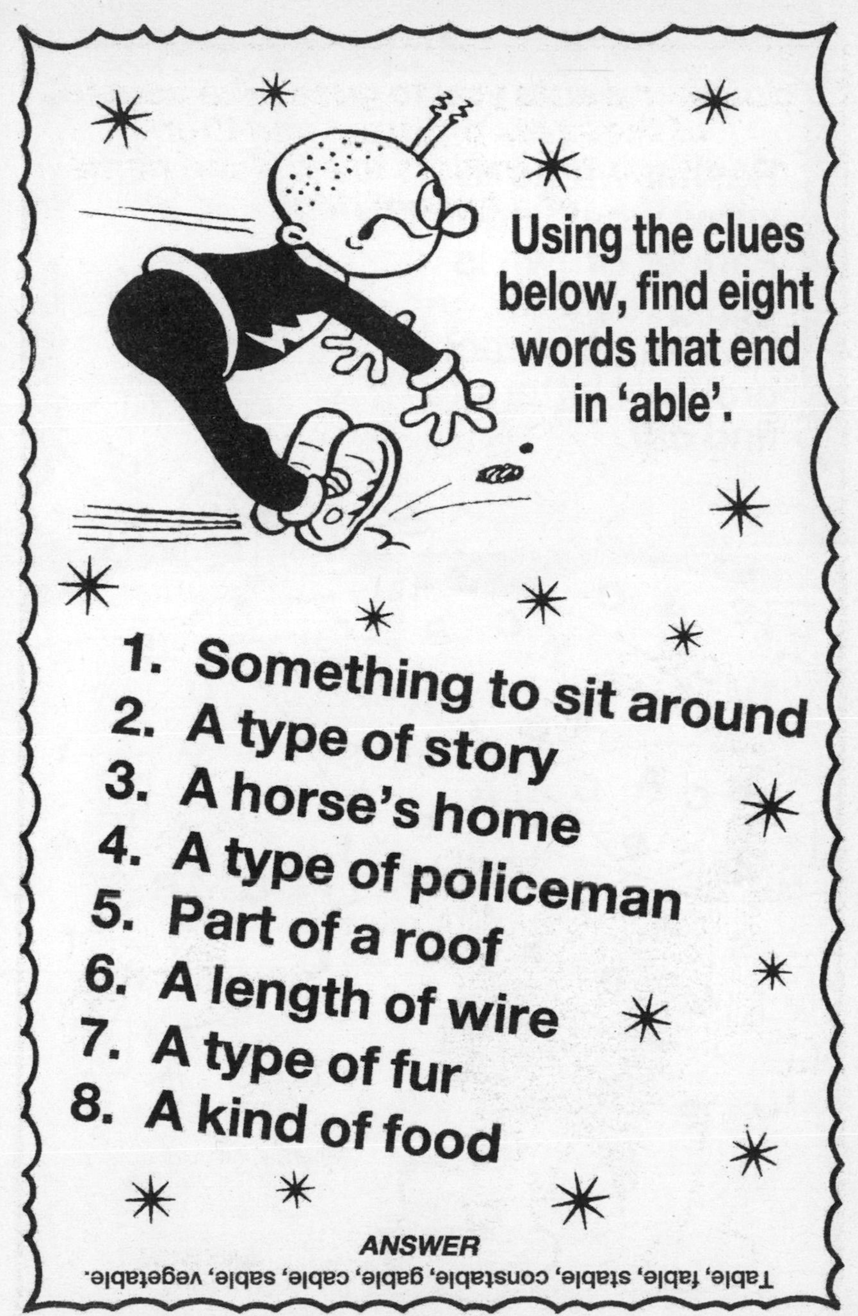
Using the clues below, find eight words that end in 'able'.
1. Something to sit around
2. A type of story
3. A horse's home
4. A type of policeman
5. Part of a roof
6. A length of wire
7. A type of fur
8. A kind of food
ANSWER
Table, fable, stable, constable, gable, cable, sable, vegetable.

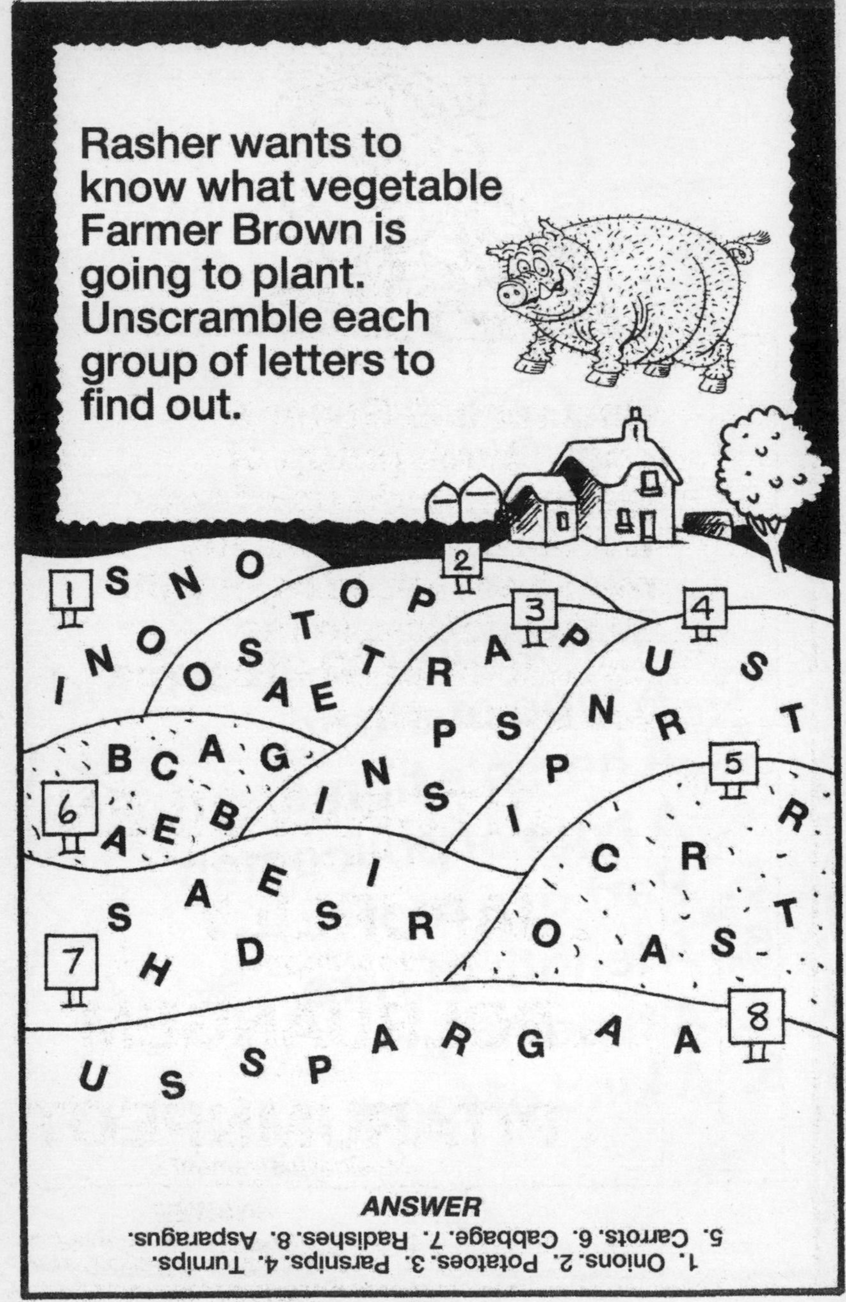
Rasher wants to know what vegetable Farmer Brown is going to plant. Unscramble each group of letters to find out.
ANSWER
1. Onions. 2. Potatoes. 3. Parsnips. 4. Turnips.
5. Carrots. 6. Cabbage. 7. Radishes. 8. Asparagus.

Unscramble Roger's code. Each group of letters is made up of two words. Both words still read from left to right with all their letters in the correct order. We've given you some clues.

1. **BITCRAYCILEN**
   Types of transport.
2. **JAPURLILY**
   Months of the year.
3. **POLRUANGEM**
   Fruit.
4. **PITARUMNPEOT**
   Musical instruments.

ANSWER

1. Bicycle, train. 2. July, April.
3. Plum, orange. 4. Piano, trumpet.

The Bash Street Kids are going to the zoo. Rearrange the groups of letters below to see which animals they can see.

ONIL TELNAEOP

YENKOM FRAGIEF

FLUBOAF YENHA

ANSWER

Lion, antelope, monkey, giraffe, buffalo, hyena.

By moving from square to square in any direction and using each letter only once, you can spell a five-word sentence. it's not too difficult!
I E N O
S T H S
T N I R
O H A D
ANSWER
Start off at "T" in the second line to read "This one is not hard".

Change one letter in each word below to spell the names of 10 sea creatures.
CACKLE
SHANK
WHELP
SQUAD
TUNE
CLAY
BRAWN
LONGER
WHINING
WHOLE
ANSWER
Cockle, Shark, Whelk, Squid, Tuna, Clam, Prawn, Conger, Whiting, Whale.

Print any 12 words in the circle, all starting with "S" and ending with "E".
S
E E E E E E E E E E E E
ANSWER
Scare, scene, shape, shine,
shore, snore, spine, stare,
stone, store, stove, swine.

A wordsquare contains words that read the same across and down. Use the list of words to make two wordsquares, each containing the word EGGS.

DREW **GOAL**
EGGS **RAGE**
EGGS **SLAP**
GALA **WEST**

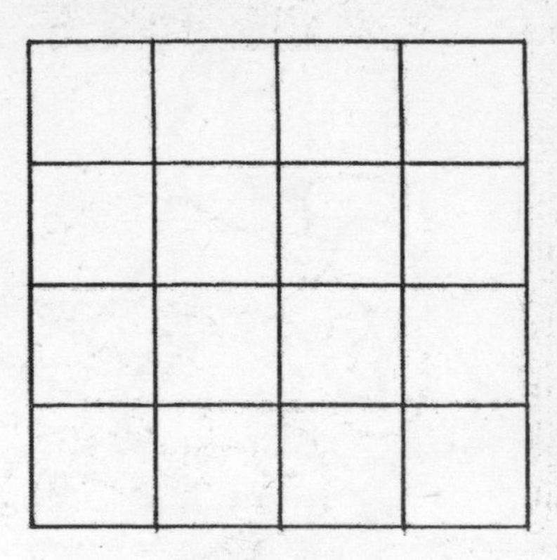

ANSWER

D	R	E	W
R	A	G	E
E	G	G	S
W	E	S	T

E	G	G	S
G	O	A	L
G	A	L	A
S	L	A	P

Spell two animals, a bird and a fish, by using only the letters in the word

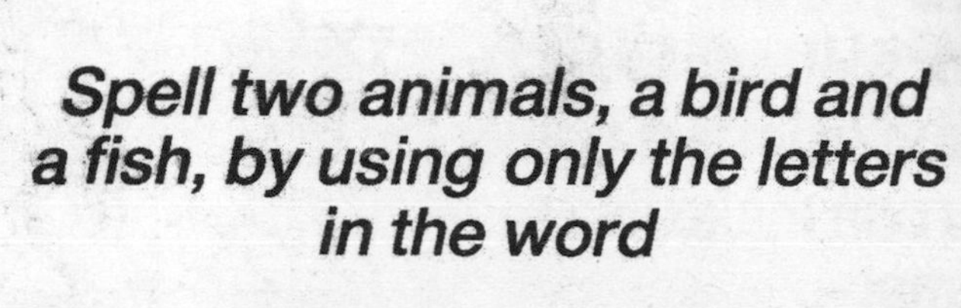

CLOWNING

ANSWER

Lion, cow, owl and ling.

Teacher knows there's no such animal as a GIZCH but if you add one of these letters to each group of letters below you can make five real animals.

ANSWER

HORSE, TIGER, BISON, ZEBRA, CAMEL.